Illustrations Credits

All illustrations © K12 Inc. unless otherwise noted

About K12 Inc.

K12 Inc., a technology-based education company, is the nation's leading provider of proprietary curriculum and online education programs to students in grades K–12. K^{12} provides its curriculum and academic services to online schools, traditional classrooms, blended school programs, and directly to families. K12 Inc. also operates the K^{12} International Academy, an accredited, diploma-granting online private school serving students worldwide. K^{12}'s mission is to provide any child the curriculum and tools to maximize success in life, regardless of geographic, financial, or demographic circumstances. K12 Inc. is accredited by CITA. More information can be found at www.K12.com.

ISBN: 978-1-60153-085-1
Printed by RR Donnelley, Shenzhen, China, March 2012, Lot 032012

Contents

Whole Number Sense

Whole Number Operations

Applications of Operations

Fraction Sense

Measurement

Fraction Operations

Decimals and Equality with Fractions

Probability and Data

Mathematical Reasoning

Geometry

Rational Numbers

Algebra Thinking

Perimeter and Area Formulas

Formulas for Area (A)

Formulas for Area (B)

Compare Area and Perimeter

Numbers Through 100,000,000

Read and Write Numbers

Memory Jogger

Millions			Thousands				hundreds	tens	ones
hundred millions	ten millions	millions	hundred thousands	ten thousands	thousands		hundreds	tens	ones
	5	1	0	2	8		6	9	3

The standard form of the number is 51,028,693.
The word form is fifty-one million, twenty-eight thousand, six hundred ninety-three.

Write the number in standard form.

1. twelve million, three hundred ninety-two thousand, six hundred five

2. seventy-four million, eight thousand, one hundred forty-three

3. one million, nine hundred thirteen thousand

4. five million, twenty-three thousand, eight hundred five

5. one hundred twenty-five thousand

Write the word form of the number.

6. 62,008,370   7. 90,009,009   8. 5,093,901

Read the number aloud.

9. 55,918,000   10. 1,069,000   11. 249,000

T R Y   I T

Choose the word form of the number.

12. 6,601,490

    A. six million, six hundred ten thousand, one hundred forty-three

    B. six million, six hundred thousand, one hundred ninety

    C. six million, six hundred one thousand, four hundred ninety

    D. sixty million, six hundred one thousand, four hundred ninety

13. 237,730

    A. two hundred thirty-seven thousand, seven hundred thirty

    B. two million, thirty-seven thousand, seven hundred thirty

    C. two hundred thirty-seven thousand, three hundred seventy

    D. two hundred thirty-seven million

14. 45,600,000

    A. forty-five million, sixty thousand   B. forty-five million, six hundred thousand

    C. forty-five million, sixty   D. forty-five million, six thousand

15. Which of these word forms names the number 25,556,000?

    A. twenty-five million, five hundred fifty-six thousand

    B. twenty-five million, five hundred fifty-six

    C. twenty-five thousand, five hundred fifty-six

    D. twenty-five thousand, fifty-six

Read the story problem and follow the directions.

16. The moon is approximately three hundred eighty-four thousand, four hundred kilometers from the earth. Write this number in standard form.

    84,400

17. There were twenty-seven million, four hundred forty thousand, three hundred twenty-one apples in the orchard's harvest. Write this number in standard form.

18. About three million, seven hundred sixty-two thousand people attended baseball games at Yankee Stadium in 2008. Write this number in standard form.

    3,762

19. Write this number in standard form: sixty-six million, nine hundred thirty-one thousand, seventy.

Expanded Form Through 100,000,000

Numbers in Expanded Form

Worked Examples

You can use a place-value chart to help you write numbers in expanded form two different ways.

PROBLEM Write the number 50,873,902 in expanded form two different ways—with words and numbers and with numbers only

SOLUTION Show 50,873,902 in the place-value chart

Millions			Thousands				hundreds	tens	ones
hundred millions	ten millions	millions	hundred thousands	ten thousands	thousands		hundreds	tens	ones
5	0		8	7	3		9	0	2

1 Line up the number 50,873,902 below the place-value chart.

2 Find the place-value position of each digit.

3 Write the digits followed by their place value in order from left to right across the page with + symbols between them.
5 ten millions + 8 hundred thousands + 7 ten thousands + 3 thousands + 9 hundreds + 2 ones

4 Replace the word forms with the value of the digits.
50,000,000 + 800,000 + 70,000 + 3,000 + 900 + 2

ANSWER 5 ten millions + 8 hundred thousands + 7 ten thousands + 3 thousands + 9 hundreds + 2 ones
50,000,000 + 800,000 + 70,000 + 3,000 + 900 + 2

Write the number in expanded form two different ways: (a) with words and numbers; (b) with numbers only.

1. 82,936

2. 4,120,398

3. 87,072,374

4. 30,046,007

LEARN

Worked Examples

You can use a place-value chart to help you write numbers in expanded form two different ways.

PROBLEM Write $70,000,000 + 8,000,000 + 30,000 + 1,000 + 900 + 90 + 6$ in standard form.

SOLUTION 1 Use a place-value chart. Write digits from the expanded number below their place value. If a place value is missing from the expanded form, write a 0 in that place-value position.

Millions			Thousands					
hundred millions	ten millions	millions	hundred thousands	ten thousands	thousands	hundreds	tens	ones
	7	8	0	3	1	9	9	6

SOLUTION 2 Line up the numbers vertically and add.

$$\begin{array}{r} 70,000,000 \\ 8,000,000 \\ 30,000 \\ 1,000 \\ 900 \\ 90 \\ + \qquad 6 \\ \hline 78,031,996 \end{array}$$

ANSWER 78,031,996

Use your place-value chart to write the number in standard form.

5. $800,000 + 70,000 + 5,000 + 900 + 30 + 6$ ~~8.8573,600~~

6. 4 ten millions + 3 millions + 7 thousands + 8 hundreds + 5 ones

7. 7 millions + 8 hundred thousands + 3 ten thousands + 6 thousands

8. $20,000,000 + 7,000,000 + 800,000 + 30,000 + 6,000 + 400 + 20 + 9$

LEARN

Expanded Form Through 100,000,000

Expanded Form

Memory Jogger

A place-value chart can help you locate the place-value position of each digit in a number so you can find the values of every digit. Then use the values to write the number in expanded form.

Millions				Thousands						
hundred millions	ten millions	millions	,	hundred thousands	ten thousands	thousands	,	hundreds	tens	ones

Choose the expanded form.

1. 29,123,300

   A. $20,000,000 + 9,000,000 + 1,000,000 + 2,000 + 300 + 30$

   B. $20,000,000 + 9,000,000 + 100,000 + 20,000 + 3,000 + 300$

   C. $200,000 + 90,000 + 1,000 + 200 + 30 + 3$

   D. $2,000,000 + 9,000,000 + 123 + 3$

2. 86,090,054

   A. $80,000,000 + 6,000,000 + 900,000 + 500 + 4$

   B. $80,000,000 + 600,000 + 9,000 + 50 + 4$

   C. $80,000,000 + 6,000,000 + 90,000 + 50 + 4$

   D. $80,000,000 + 6,000,000 + 90,000 + 500 + 40$

3. 22,081,000

   A. $20,000,000 + 2,000,000 + 80,000 + 1,000$

   B. $200,000,000 + 2,000,000 + 80,000 + 1,000$

   C. $20,000,000 + 2,000,000 + 800,000 + 10,000$

   D. $20,000,000 + 2,000,000 + 8,000 + 1,000$

TRY IT

4. 4,310,000

    A. 4 millions + 3 hundred thousands + 1 ten thousand

    B. 4 millions + 3 hundred thousands + 1 thousand

    C. 4 ten millions + 3 hundred thousands + 1 ten thousand

    D. 4 ten millions + 3 million + 1 ten thousand

Choose the standard form.

5. 20,000,000 + 300,000 + 60,000 + 500 + 40 + 2

    A. 20,365,042   B. 23,060,542   C. 20,365,420   D. 20,360,542

6. 4 hundred thousands + 6 ten thousands + 3 hundreds + 8 ones

    A. 460,308   B. 4,638,000   C. 463,008   D. 4,060,308

7. 3 ten millions + 1 million + 2 hundred thousands + 4 ten thousands

    A. 31,240,000   B. 31,204,000   C. 31,024,000   D. 31,002,400

Write the standard form.

8. 40,000,000 + 200,000 + 8,000 + 9

9. 9 ten millions + 7 millions + 4 hundred thousands + 5 ten thousands

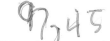

Write the expanded form.

10. 784,893

11. 47,090,700

12. 4,809,060

13. 56,323,759

Write the number in expanded form with numbers only.

14. 5,834,000

15. 3,015,000

16. 63,432,000

TRY IT

Compare and Order Greater Numbers (A)

Comparing Numbers

Compare the numbers. Write $<$, $>$, or $=$.

1. 45,903,784 ☐ 45,912,081

2. 867,341 ☐ 1,297,343

3. 336,983 ☐ 334,883

4. 18,928,201 ☐ 18,928,201

5. 67,203,245 ☐ 39,874,192

6. 7,893,034 ☐ 7,893,078

Write a digit that makes the comparison sentence true.

7. 9,2 ☐ 3,809 $<$ 9,233,879

8. 1,529,087 $<$ 1,☐34,220

9. 891,☐98 $<$ 891,543

10. 2,346,487 $<$ 2,3☐7,269

11. 286,593 $<$ 2☐6,275 $<$ 297,801

Write the place-value position that you would use to decide which number is greater.

12. 16,349,333 $>$ 16,140,102

13. 4,893,998 $<$ 13,894,944

14. 34,874,983 $>$ 34,874,763

TRY IT

Compare the numbers and choose the answer.

15. 7,635,491 and 7,596,223

    A. $7,635,491 = 7,596,223$

    B. $7,635,491 > 7,596,223$

    C. $7,635,491 < 7,596,223$

16. 365,724 and 362,986

    A. $365,724 < 362,986$

    B. $365,724 = 362,986$

    C. $365,724 > 362,986$

17. 25,645,248 and 25,645,248

    A. $25,645,248 = 25,645,248$

    B. $25,645,248 < 25,645,248$

    C. $25,645,248 > 25,645,248$

18. 786,729 and 789,542

    A. $786,729 > 789,542$

    B. $786,729 < 789,542$

    C. $786,729 = 789,542$

19. 573,426 and 593,862

    A. $573,426 = 593,862$

    B. $573,426 > 593,862$

    C. $573,426 < 593,862$

20. 100,000,000 and 98,645,895

    A. $100,000,000 = 98,645,895$

    B. $100,000,000 > 98,645,895$

    C. $100,000,000 < 98,645,895$

TRY IT

Using Boundary Numbers for Rounding

Explain and Justify Rounding

Worked Examples

You can round a whole number by using a number line and by using place value.

PROBLEM 1 Round 87,125,737 to the nearest million.

SOLUTION 1 Use a number line.

87,125,737

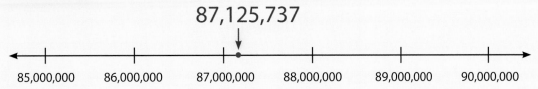

On the number line, 87,125,737 is closer to 87,000,000 than to 88,000,000.

SOLUTION 2 Use place value.

1 Underline the digit in the "rounding place," or the millions. Circle the digit in the place-value position to its right, in the hundred thousands place.

Millions			Thousands					
hundred millions	ten millions	millions	hundred thousands	ten thousands	thousands	hundreds	tens	ones
	8	7̲	⟨1⟩	2	5	7	3	7

2 If the circled digit is greater than or equal to 5, the digit in the rounding place increases by 1. To show its value, each digit to its right becomes 0.

The circled digit 1 is not greater than or equal to 5, so move to the next step.

3 If the circled digit is less than 5, the digit in the rounding place stays the same. To show its true value, each digit to its right becomes 0.

The circled digit $1 < 5$, so the 7 in the millions place stays the same. Each digit to its right becomes 0 to show its true value. So the rounded number is 87,000,000.

ANSWER To the nearest million, 87,125,737 rounds to 87,000,000.

L E A R N

PROBLEM 2 Round 87,125,737 to the nearest ten thousand.

SOLUTION 1 Use a number line.

87,125,737

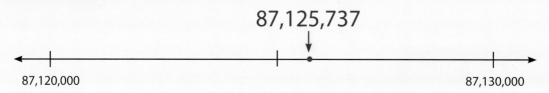

87,120,000   87,130,000

On the number line, 87,125,737 is closer to 87,130,000 than to 87,120,000.

SOLUTION 2 Use place value.

1 Underline the digit in the "rounding place," or the ten thousands.
Circle the digit in the place-value position to its right, in the thousands place.

Millions			Thousands					
hundred millions	ten millions	millions	hundred thousands	ten thousands	thousands	hundreds	tens	ones
	8	7	1	2	5	7	3	7

2 If the circled digit is greater than or equal to 5, the digit in the rounding place increases by 1. To show its value, each digit to its right becomes 0.

The circled digit 5 = 5, so the 2 in the ten thousands place increases to 3, and each digit to its right becomes 0 to show its true value. So the rounded number is 87,130,000.

ANSWER To the nearest ten thousand, 87,125,737 rounds to 87,130,000.

Round each number and explain how you found your answer.

1. Round 43,620,751 to the nearest ten million.

2. What is 3,627,137 rounded to the nearest ten thousand?

3. What is 62,500 rounded to the nearest thousand?

Round 25,471,435 to the nearest place value.

4. ten million

5. million

6. hundred thousand

7. ten thousand

Using Boundary Numbers for Rounding

Round Whole Numbers

Write the answer.

1. Round 48,620,751 to the nearest ten million.

2. What is 5,469,218 rounded to the nearest ten thousand?

3. What is 12,500 rounded to the nearest thousand?

4. Redwood National Park contains 75,452 acres.
   Round this number to the nearest hundred.

5. What is 795,321 rounded to the nearest hundred thousand?

Round 34,394,329 to the nearest place value.

6. ten million

7. million

8. hundred thousand

9. ten thousand

10. thousand

11. hundred

12. ten

Choose the answer.

13. An airline reported that it flew 16,341,500 passengers in a nine-month period.
    Which number is rounded to the nearest hundred thousand?

    A. 16,300,000

    B. 16,340,000

    C. 16,400,000

    D. 16,000,000

14. Which shows 10,917,652 rounded to the nearest million?

    A. 900,000

    B. 9,000,000

    C. 10,000,000

    D. 11,000,000

© K12 Inc. All rights reserved.

T R Y   I T

15. A reporter rounded the number of homes that were without power in Maine after a winter ice storm. The reporter said 250,000, which was correctly rounded to the nearest ten thousand. Which number could **not** be the number that was rounded?

    A. 252,000

    B. 250,925

    C. 246,000

    D. 243,000

16. Which shows 88,656,232 rounded to the nearest ten million?

    A. 80,000,000

    B. 88,000,000

    C. 90,000,000

    D. 88,700,000

17. Round 4,481,594 to the nearest million.

    A. 4,000,000

    B. 4,400,000

    C. 4,500,000

    D. 5,000,000

18. Walter was asked to round a number to the nearest ten million. He correctly wrote 50,000,000. Which number could be the number Walter was asked to round?

    A. 54,866,196

    B. 57,890,001

    C. 58,787,850

    D. 59,887,105

Read the problem and follow the directions.

19. Sandra wants to round 359,825 to the nearest ten thousand. Explain what she should do and write the correct answer.

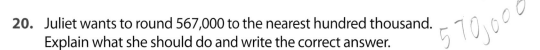

400,000

20. Juliet wants to round 567,000 to the nearest hundred thousand. Explain what she should do and write the correct answer.

570,000

21. Taylor and Martha rounded the number 847,550 to the nearest thousand. Taylor said the answer is 848,000. Martha said the answer is 847,000. Who is correct? Explain.

22. Maya and Frankie rounded the number 24,317 to the nearest ten. Maya said the answer is 24,320. Frankie said the answer is 24,310. Who is correct?

23. A department store has donated school supplies to 107,547 schools for many years. Round this number to the nearest thousand.

TRY IT

Unit Review

Checkpoint Practice

Answer the question.

1. My number has a
   5 in the thousands place
   3 in the ten thousands place
   7 in the millions place
   4 in the tens place
   2 in the hundreds place
   0 in the hundred thousands place
   6 in the ones place.
   What is my number?

   7,350,246

2. The National Museum of American History has 3,309,000 objects in its collection. Round this number to the nearest million.

   2,000,000

3. What is 95,321 rounded to the nearest thousand?

   100,000

4. Write a number in the box to make this statement true.
   4,7 ? 6,245 > 4,739,825

   4,746,245 > 4,739,825

Choose the answer.

5. What is the value of 9 in the number 25,938?

   A. 90

   B. 900

   C. 9,000

   D. 90,000

6. Which number has a 5 in the ten millions place?

   A. 16,531,892

   B. 32,645,147

   C. 46,752,143

   D. 56,842,723

7. Which number means 70,000,000 + 6,000,000 + 100,000 + 2,000?

   A. 76,120,000

   B. 76,102,000

   C. 7,610,200

   D. 761,200

8. Which shows 8,037,000 written in expanded form?

   A. 8,000,000 + 300,000 + 7,000

   B. 8,000,000 + 300,000 + 700

   C. 8,000,000 + 30,000 + 7,000

   D. 8,000,000 + 300,000 + 70,000

WHOLE NUMBER SENSE

13

9. Round 156,274 to the nearest hundred thousand.

    A. 100,000

    B. 150,000

    C. 200,000

    D. 260,000

10. Which means the same as 21,128,000?

    A. 2 ten millions + 1 million + 1 hundred thousand + 2 hundred thousands + 8 thousands

    B. 2 ten millions + 1 million + 1 hundred thousand + 2 ten thousands + 8 thousands

    C. 2 hundred millions + 1 ten million + 1 hundred thousand + 2 ten thousands + 8 thousands

    D. 2 hundred millions + 1 million + 1 hundred thousand + 2 ten thousands + 8 thousands

11. Which shows 64,192,000 written in words?

    A. sixty-four million, one hundred ninety-two thousand

    B. sixty-four million, one hundred ninety-two

    C. sixty-four thousand, one hundred ninety-two

    D. sixty-four million, one hundred nineteen thousand, two

12. Which shows 42,392,000 written in words?

    A. forty-two million, three hundred ninety-two

    B. forty-two million, three hundred ninety-two thousand

    C. forty-two thousand, three hundred ninety-two

    D. forty-two million, three hundred two thousand

13. Which of these numbers is 8,033,000?

    A. eighty thousand, thirty-three

    B. eighty thousand, thirty-three hundred

    C. eight million, thirty-three thousand

    D. eighty million, thirty-three thousand

Write in standard form.

14. eighteen million, four hundred forty-two thousand, seven hundred twenty-five

15. nine hundred twenty-two thousand, one hundred twenty-one

16. A few years ago Mumbai, India, had a population of approximately thirteen million, six hundred sixty-two thousand.

17. The average person sleeps around one hundred ninety-four thousand, eight hundred twenty hours in a lifetime.

Choose the answer.

18. Mattie was asked to round a number to the nearest thousand. She correctly wrote 78,000. Which number could **not** be the number Mattie was asked to round?

   A. 78,115   B. 77,990

   C. 77,560   D. 77,269

19. Which set of numbers is in order from least to greatest?

   A. 6,373,926 < 6,374,794 < 6,374,852

   B. 6,373,926 < 6,374,852 < 6,374,794

   C. 6,374,852 < 6,373,926 < 6,374,794

20. Joe wants to order the numbers 79,428,765; 78,563,254; and 79,418,932 from greatest to least. Which statement is correct?

   A. 79,428,765 > 78,563,254 > 79,418,932

   B. 79,428,765 > 79,418,932 > 78,563,254

   C. 78,563,254 > 79,418,932 > 79,428,765

21. Compare the numbers 248,936 and 250,726 using <, >, or =.

   A. 248,936 = 250,726

   B. 248,936 > 250,726

   C. 248,936 < 250,726

Answer the question.

22. What digit can replace the ? to make this comparison sentence true?
   648,523 < 6 ? 9,246 < 658,523

Estimate Sums and Differences (A)

Estimating Sums

Choose the best two numbers to use to estimate the sum.

1. 293,345 + 1,294,333
   A. 300,000
   B. 1,000,000
   C. 2,000,000
   D. 30,000

2. 1,984,345 + 2,398,352
   A. 20,000,000
   B. 10,000,000
   C. 2,000,000
   D. 2,400,000

3. 56,903 + 30,452
   A. 30,000
   B. 500,000
   C. 30,452
   D. 57,000

Use the friendly numbers from above to estimate the sum.
Use a number line if you wish.

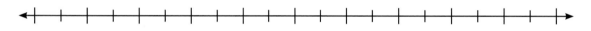

4. 293,345 + 1,294,333

5. 1,984,345 + 2,398,352

6. 56,903 + 30,452

Use friendly numbers to estimate the sum.
Write the friendly numbers you used and your estimate.

7. 1,209,452 + 12,453,935

8. 16,935 + 398,421

9. 347,194 + 923,734

Use a number line to estimate the following sum.

10. There were 20,208 people at the soccer stadium before the game started. Another 12,962 people came into the stadium after the game started. How many people were at the stadium in total?

20,200 21,200 22,200 23,200 24,200 25,200 26,200 27,200 28,200 29,200 30,200 31,200 32,200 33,200

TRY IT

Choose the answer.

11. There were 2,598 people in the amusement park before 9:30 a.m. Another 824 people entered the amusement park between 9:30 and 10:30. Which number line shows the best estimate for the number of people in the amusement park at 10:30 a.m.?

A.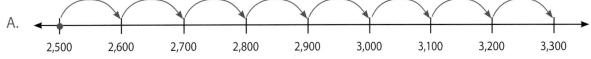
2,500   2,600   2,700   2,800   2,900   3,000   3,100   3,200   3,300

B.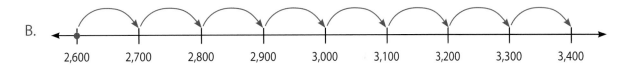
2,600   2,700   2,800   2,900   3,000   3,100   3,200   3,300   3,400

C.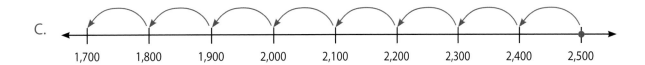
1,700   1,800   1,900   2,000   2,100   2,200   2,300   2,400   2,500

D.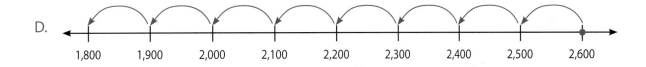
1,800   1,900   2,000   2,100   2,200   2,300   2,400   2,500   2,600

12. Which number line shows the best estimate for the sum of 458 and 108?

A.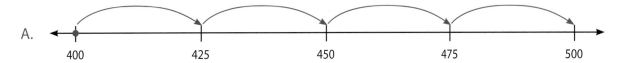
400   425   450   475   500

B.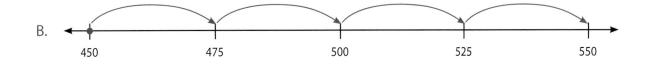
450   475   500   525   550

C.
300   325   350   375   400

D.
350   375   400   425   450

T R Y   I T

Estimate Sums and Differences (B)

Estimating Differences

Choose the best two numbers to use to estimate the difference.

1. 354,008 − 203,004
   - A. 350,000
   - B. 1,000,000
   - C. 200,000
   - D. 30,000

2. 3,490,223 − 899,343
   - A. 30,000,000
   - B. 90,000
   - C. 900,000
   - D. 3,500,000

3. 9,341 − 8,394
   - A. 9,000
   - B. 100,000
   - C. 80,000
   - D. 8,000

Use the friendly numbers from above to estimate the difference. Use the number line if you wish.

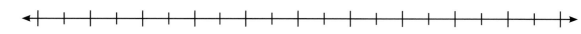

4. 354,008 − 203,004

5. 3,490,223 − 899,343

6. 9,341 − 8,394

Use friendly numbers to estimate the difference.
Write the friendly numbers you used and your estimate.

7. 78,340 − 45,300

8. 193,392 − 54,698

9. 394,394 − 108,399

10. 6,944 − 3,298

11. 34,894,334 − 5,633,887

12. 75,004 − 22,985

13. 599 − 208

14. 9,211 − 4,877

15. 8,705,665 − 1,537,947

TRY IT

Use the number line to estimate the difference.

16. 7,934 − 3,686

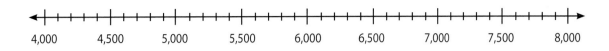

4,000 4,500 5,000 5,500 6,000 6,500 7,000 7,500 8,000

17. 8,342 − 539

7,700 7,800 7,900 8,000 8,100 8,200 8,300 8,400

18. 456 − 62

380 390 400 410 420 430 440 450 460 470 480

Use the number line to solve the problem.

19. The Mauna Kea volcano in Hawaii is 33,504 feet tall from the ocean floor to its peak. The Aloha peak is 1,206 feet tall. Estimate about how much taller the Mauna Kea peak is than the Aloha peak.

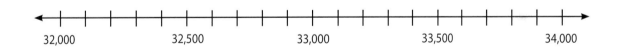

32,000 32,500 33,000 33,500 34,000

20. The Yosemite Falls are 2,425 feet tall. The Shannon Falls are 1,105 feet tall. Estimate about how much taller the Yosemite Falls are than the Shannon Falls.

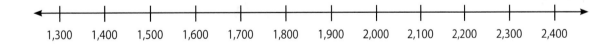

1,300 1,400 1,500 1,600 1,700 1,800 1,900 2,000 2,100 2,200 2,300 2,400

21. The Salto Angel waterfall in Venezuela is 3,212 feet tall. The James Bruce waterfall in Canada is 2,755 feet tall. Estimate about how much taller the Salto Angel waterfall is than the James Bruce waterfall.

400 1,200 2,200 3,200

Multiply by 2-Digit Numbers (A)

Practice 2-Digit Multiplication

Find the product.

1. Multiply 95 by 32.

$$\begin{array}{r} 95 \\ \times\ 32 \\ \hline 3040 \end{array}$$

2. Multiply 16 by 14.

$$\begin{array}{r} 16 \\ \times\ 14 \\ \hline 224 \end{array}$$

3. Multiply 42 by 36.

$$\begin{array}{r} 42 \\ \times\ 36 \\ \hline 1512 \end{array}$$

4. Multiply 39 by 21.

$$\begin{array}{r} 39 \\ \times\ 21 \\ \hline 819 \end{array}$$

Explain how to solve the problem.

5. Multiply 12 by 17. 204

I took 17 times 12

6. Multiply 57 by 48.

Choose the number sentence that solves the problem.

7. One month Yolanda planted 24 flowers. The next month her sister planted 12 times as many flowers. How many flowers did Yolanda's sister plant?

   A. $24 \div 12 = 2$

   B. $24 + 12 = 36$

   C. $24 \times 12 = 288$

   D. $24 - 12 = 12$

8. Jenna played in 24 basketball games. At each game she scored 12 points. How many points did Jenn score in all?

   A. $24 \times 12 = 248$

   B. $24 \times 12 = 288$

   C. $24 \times 12 = 296$

   D. $24 \times 12 = 396$

TRY IT

Multiply by 2-Digit Numbers (B)

Multiply Greater Numbers

Worked Examples

You can multiply greater numbers by finding the sum of partial products.

PROBLEM
$$\begin{array}{r} 237 \\ \times\ 25 \\ \hline \end{array}$$

SOLUTION

1 Multiply 5×7, 5×30, and 5×200.

$$\begin{array}{r} 200 + 30 + 7 \\ \times\ \ \ 20 + 5 \\ \hline 1{,}000 + 150 + 35 = 1{,}185 \end{array}$$

2 Multiply 20×7, 20×30, and 20×200.

$$\begin{array}{r} 200 + 30 + 7 \\ \times\ \ \ 20 + 5 \\ \hline 4{,}000 + 600 + 140 = 4{,}740 \end{array}$$

3 Add the partial products from Steps 1 and 2.

$$\begin{array}{r} 200 + 30 + 7 \\ \times\ \ \ 20 + 5 \\ \hline 1{,}000 + 150 + 35 = 1{,}185 \\ 4{,}000 + 600 + 140 = 4{,}740 \\ \hline 5{,}925 \end{array}$$

$$\begin{array}{r} 200 + 30 + 7 \\ \times\ \ \ 20 + 5 \\ \hline 5 \times 7 = 35 \\ 5 \times 30 = 150 \\ 5 \times 200 = 1{,}000 \\ 20 \times 7 = 140 \\ 20 \times 30 = 600 \\ 20 \times 200 = +\ 4{,}000 \\ \hline 5{,}925 \end{array}$$

ANSWER $237 \times 25 = 5{,}925$

Solve.

1. There are 274 sheets of paper in one stack. There are 53 stacks.
   How many sheets of paper are there in all?
   3,722

2. For each gallon of gas Rob put in the gas tank of his car, his car
   traveled 23 miles. If Rob's car used 123 gallons of gas,
   how many miles did it travel?

3. Every time Rufus fetches the ball and brings it back, he runs
   26 meters. If Rufus fetches the ball 1,257 times during the summer,
   how many meters will he have run?

4.   184   5.   98   6.   210
     $\times$ 45 $\times$ 21 $\times$ 67
      8,290   2,058   14,070

Read the problem and follow the directions.

7. Sunny had 24 boxes of apples. Each box held 184 apples.
   How many apples did she have in all?
   Find the answer and explain your work.   4,416

8. Sarah delivered 132 newspapers each week for 25 weeks.
   What is the total number of newspapers she delivered?
   Explain how to solve the problem.   3300

LEARN

Different Ways to Divide (A)

Find Quotients

Add to find the quotient.

1. $964 \div 4 = \underline{\ ?\ }$

2. $5{,}490 \div 6 = \underline{\ ?\ }$

Subtract to find the quotient.

3. $8\overline{)4{,}528}$

4. $3\overline{)279}$

Divide. Record the quotient above the division bracket.

5. $5\overline{)4{,}145}$

6. $7\overline{)238}$

Solve.

7. Charlie has 756 books arranged in 6 different bookcases. If each bookcase has the same number of books, how many books are in each one?

8. A sports shop has 1,944 baseball caps in stock. They are stored in boxes with 8 caps in a box. How many boxes of baseball caps does the store have?

9. Which division problem is incorrect? Explain the mistake in the problem.

A.
```
        356
  4)1,024
  - 1,200
  ───────
      224
    - 200
  ───────
       24
     - 24
  ───────
        0
```

B.
```
        256
  4)1,024
  -   800
  ───────
      224
    - 200
  ───────
       24
     - 24
  ───────
        0
```

TRY IT

10. Divide. $6\overline{)420}$

    A. 7   B. 70

    C. 80   D. 700

11. What is the quotient of 4,564 divided by 7?

    A. 652   B. 642

    C. 256   D. $65\frac{2}{7}$

12. Divide 375 by 5.

13. Divide. $3\overline{)2,562}$

14. Divide 6,265 by 7. Explain how to solve the problem.

15. Divide 390 by 6. Explain how to solve the problem.

16. Rachelle solved this division problem.
Explain the mistake Rachelle made and give the correct answer.

$$
\begin{array}{r}
54 \\
8\overline{)360} \\
-320 \\
\hline
40 \\
-40 \\
\hline
0
\end{array}
$$

17. Which number sentence solves the problem?
Tom feeds his rabbits sunflower seeds. He uses 450 ounces in 6 months.
How many ounces of seeds does Tom use each month?

    A. $450 \div 6 = 57$ B. $450 \div 6 = 75$

    C. $450 \times 6 = 2,400$ D. $450 \times 6 = 2,700$

18. Jessie has 152 pencils. She wants to put them into packages of 8 pencils each.
How many packages of 8 pencils can Jessie make? Explain how to solve the problem.

TRY IT

Different Ways to Divide (B)

Remainders in Division

Worked Examples

You can show a remainder in a division problem two ways. How a remainder affects the final answer to a story problem depends on what the problem asks for.

PROBLEM Divide: $139 \div 6 = ?$

SOLUTION 1 Estimate how many times 6 divides 139.

$$
\begin{array}{r}
23 \text{ r 1 or } 23\frac{1}{6} \\
6\overline{)139} \\
-120 \\
\hline
19 \\
-18 \\
\hline
1
\end{array}
$$

Since 20 times 6 is 120, 6 divides 139 about 20 times (or 2 tens). Place the 2 above the tens place of the dividend.

Multiply 20 by 6. $20 \times 6 = 120$

Next, subtract $139 - 120$ to get 19. Divide 19 by 6. Write 3 above the ones place of the dividend.

Multiply 3 by 6. $3 \times 6 = 18$

$19 - 18 = 1$; 1 is less than the divisor 6, so 1 is the remainder.

SOLUTION 2 Make or draw a model.

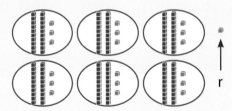

ANSWER 23 r 1 or $23\frac{1}{6}$

Divide. If there is a remainder, express the quotient with a remainder and then as a mixed number.

1. $6\overline{)457}$

2. $8\overline{)983}$

3. $9\overline{)345}$

4. $4\overline{)996}$

LEARN

Worked Examples

PROBLEM 1 Marty is packing 141 books in boxes. Each box holds 6 books. How many boxes does Marty need to pack all the books?

SOLUTION

1 $141 \div 6 = 23$ r 3 or $23\frac{3}{6}$

2 Marty has 3 books left over after he packs 23 boxes. Marty needs 1 more box for the 3 books.

3 So Marty needs 24 boxes to pack all the books.

ANSWER Marty needs 24 boxes.

PROBLEM 2 A clerk is arranging 141 toys on shelves at the toy store. If he puts 6 toys on a shelf, the shelf is full. How many shelves can the clerk fill?

SOLUTION

1 $141 \div 6 = 23$ r 3 or $23\frac{3}{6}$

2 The 3 toys that are left over will not fill a shelf.

3 So the clerk can fill only 23 shelves.

ANSWER The clerk can fill 23 shelves.

PROBLEM 3 An athlete ran for 141 minutes. It takes her 6 minutes to run 1 block. How many blocks did the athlete run?

SOLUTION

1 $141 \div 6 = 23$ r 3 or $23\frac{3}{6}$

2 The athlete can run a fraction of a block.

3 So she ran $23\frac{3}{6}$ blocks.

ANSWER The athlete ran $23\frac{3}{6}$ blocks.

LEARN

Use the worked division problem shown here to answer Problems 5–7.

$$
\begin{array}{r}
336 \text{ r } 3 \text{ or } 336\frac{3}{4} \\
4\overline{)1{,}347} \\
-1{,}200 \\
\hline
147 \\
-120 \\
\hline
27 \\
-24 \\
\hline
3
\end{array}
$$

5. Sarah uses 1,347 ounces of clay to make 4 figures. All the figures are the same size. How many ounces of clay does Sarah use in each figure?

   $1{,}347 \div 4 = \Box$

6. There are 1,347 people waiting for a roller coaster. Each roller-coaster car holds 4 riders. How many cars will it take for all the people to have a ride?

   $1{,}347 \div 4 = \Box$

7. Kelly and her friends are beading bags to sell at a craft show. They must sew 4 beads on each bag. They have 1,347 beads. How many bags can they bead?

   $1{,}347 \div 4 = \Box$

Solve. Explain how you got your answer.

8. There are 277 players in a basketball league. There can be no more than 9 players on each team. How many teams are needed in the league?

9. A machine at a factory cuts ribbon into pieces that are 4 inches long. A worker puts 4,550 inches of ribbon in the machine. How many 4-inch pieces of ribbon will the machine cut?

LEARN

Different Ways to Divide (B)

Check Division

Worked Examples

You can check division by multiplying the quotient by the divisor and adding the remainder, if there is one.

PROBLEM Divide 316 by 6. Show how you checked your answer.

SOLUTION Estimate how many times 6 divides 316.

Since 50 times 6 is 300, 6 divides 316 about 50 times (or 5 tens). ⟶ 52 r 4 or $52\frac{4}{6}$
Place the 5 above the tens place of the dividend.

$$6\overline{)316}$$

Multiply 50 by 6. $50 \times 6 = 300$ ⟶ -300

Next, subtract $316 - 300$ to get 16. Divide 16 by 6. ⟶ 16
Write 2 above the ones place of the dividend. -12

Multiply 2 by 6. $2 \times 6 = 12$ ⟶ 4

$16 - 12 = 4$; 4 is less than the divisor 6, so 4 is the remainder. ⟶

LOOK BACK Multiply the quotient by the divisor. Then add the remainder. If the result equals the dividend, the quotient is correct.

$$
\begin{array}{rl}
52 & \leftarrow \text{quotient} \\
\times\ 6 & \leftarrow \text{divisor} \\
\hline
312 & \\
+\ 4 & \leftarrow \text{remainder} \\
\hline
316 & \leftarrow \text{dividend?}
\end{array}
$$

Write a number sentence to check each quotient. If the quotient shown is correct, write *correct*. If the quotient shown is not correct, write *not correct*.

1.
$$5\overline{)1{,}445} \quad 289?$$

2.
$$7\overline{)569} \quad 82 \text{ r } 3 \text{ or } 82\frac{3}{7}?$$

3.
$$3\overline{)2{,}227} \quad 742 \text{ r } 1 \text{ or } 742\frac{1}{3}?$$

L E A R N

Divide. If there is a remainder, express the quotient with a remainder and then as a mixed number. Then write a number sentence to check your answer.

4. $8\overline{)448}^{\,?}$

5. $2\overline{)137}^{\,?}$

6. $6\overline{)599}^{\,?}$

7. $4\overline{)1,732}^{\,?}$

8. $7\overline{)3,589}^{\,?}$

LEARN

Different Ways to Divide (B)

Divide and Check

Divide. If there is a remainder, express the quotient with a remainder and then as a mixed number.

1. $6\overline{)3,569}$

2. $9\overline{)1,806}$

Multiply to check each quotient. If the quotient shown is correct, write *correct*. If the quotient shown is not correct, write *not correct*.

3. $\overset{794 \text{ r } 4 \text{ or } 794\frac{4}{6}}{6\overline{)4,762}}$

4. $\overset{83}{3\overline{)249}}$

Divide.

5. $4\overline{)132}$

6. $8\overline{)5,889}$

Choose the answer.

7. $5\overline{)544}$

A. $18\frac{4}{5}$　　　　B. 108　　　　C. $108\frac{4}{5}$　　　　D. 1084

Solve. Explain how you got your answer.

8. Campers are all going on canoe rides. One canoe can hold 6 people. There are 207 campers. How many canoes do they need?

9. The kennel uses 577 cups of dog food in 7 days. They use the same amount of dog food each day. How many cups of dog food does the kennel use each day?

10. Divide 2,623 by 9.

11. Aimee solved this division question. Explain the mistake Aimee made and give the correct answer.

$$
\begin{array}{r}
1,312 \\
6\overline{)788} \\
-6 \\
\hline
18 \\
-18 \\
\hline
8 \\
-6 \\
\hline
2
\end{array}
$$

T R Y   I T

12. Gino is making appetizers. He needs 3 cherry tomatoes for each mini pizza he is making. He has 178 tomatoes. How many pizzas can he make?

13. Joshua has 548 photographs. His album holds 8 photographs on each page. How many pages will he need to hold all his photographs?

14. An airplane traveled 4,287 miles in 8 hours. How many miles did the airplane travel in one hour?

Read the problem and follow the directions.

15. Helene solved this division problem. Show how Helene could check her work using multiplication. Is Helene correct?

$$\begin{array}{r} 874 \\ 6\overline{)2,868} \end{array}$$

16. Caroline was asked to put numbers in the boxes to make this equation correct.

$$8\,\square\,1 \div 9 = 89$$

Caroline doesn't want to use the "guess and check" strategy. Explain a strategy that Caroline could use. Write the correct answer.

17. Nina solved this multiplication problem. Choose the expression she could use to check her work.

$$\begin{array}{r} 56 \\ \times\ 12 \\ \hline 672 \end{array}$$

A. 12×672

B. 56×672

C. $672 \div 12$

D. $56 \div 12$

TRY IT

Order of Operations (A)

Parentheses and Expressions

Worked Examples

Perform the operation or operations inside parentheses before all other operations. Changing the position of parentheses may change the value of the expression.

PROBLEM 1 $7 + 3 \times 6 + 2 = \underline{\ ?\ }$

SOLUTION

$7 + \mathbf{3} \times \mathbf{6} + 2 = ?$ ← Multiply.
$7 + \mathbf{18} + 2 = ?$ ← Add.
$\mathbf{25} + \mathbf{2} = 27$ ← Add.

ANSWER 27

PROBLEM 2 $(7 + 3) \times 6 + 2 = \underline{\ ?\ }$

SOLUTION

$\mathbf{(7 + 3)} \times 6 + 2 = ?$ ← Add inside parentheses.
$\mathbf{10} \times \mathbf{6} + 2 = ?$ ← Multiply.
$\mathbf{60} + \mathbf{2} = 62$ ← Add.

ANSWER 62

PROBLEM 3 $7 + 3 \times (6 + 2) = \underline{\ ?\ }$

SOLUTION

$7 + 3 \times \mathbf{(6 + 2)} = ?$ ← Add inside parentheses.
$7 + \mathbf{3} \times \mathbf{8} = ?$ ← Multiply.
$7 + \mathbf{24} = 31$ ← Add.

ANSWER 31

PROBLEM 4 $(7 + 3) \times (6 + 2) = \underline{\ ?\ }$

SOLUTION

$\mathbf{(7 + 3)} \times (6 + 2) = ?$ ← Add inside parentheses.
$10 \times \mathbf{(6 + 2)} = ?$ ← Add inside parentheses.
$\mathbf{10} \times \mathbf{8} = 80$ ← Multiply.

ANSWER 80

Copy the following expression into your Math Notebook three times—at the top, middle, and bottom of a blank page. Leave a few blank lines beneath each expression.

$$2 + 3 \times 4 - 1 = ?$$

1. In the top expression, put parentheses around (3×4) and evaluate.

2. In the middle expression, put parentheses around $(4 - 1)$ and evaluate.

3. In the bottom expression, put parentheses around $(2 + 3)$ and evaluate.

LEARN

Place one set of parentheses in the expression to make it true.

4. $24 + 8 \div 4 - 2 = 6$

5. $24 + 8 \div 4 - 2 = 28$

6. $6 \times 15 \div 3 + 2 = 32$

7. $6 \times 15 \div 3 + 2 = 18$

Evaluate the expression.

8. $(2 + 3) \times (4 - 1) = \underline{\ ?\ }$

9. $(4 + 20) \div (3 - 1) = \underline{\ ?\ }$

10. $(5 + 12) \times (18 \div 9) = \underline{\ ?\ }$

11. $(10 - 7) + (8 - 3) = \underline{\ ?\ }$

Write the number that makes the number sentence true.

12. $5 \times (\underline{\ ?\ } - 2) = 35$

13. $(10 \times 2) \div \underline{\ ?\ } = 2$

14. $\underline{\ ?\ } \times (3 + 5) = 32$

Write $+$, $-$, $\times$, or $\div$ to make the number sentence true.

15. $(3 \times 5) \underline{\ ?\ } 10 \div 2 = 10$

16. $2 + (5 \underline{\ ?\ } 3) - 1 = 16$

17. $4 + 7 - 3 \div 1 \underline{\ ?\ } 2 = 6$

LEARN

Order of Operations (A)

Evaluating Expressions

Memory Jogger

ORDER OF OPERATIONS

- First compute inside all parentheses.
- Next perform multiplication and division as the symbols appear from left to right.
- Then perform addition and subtraction as the symbols appear from left to right.

Solve. Explain your steps.

1. $10 \div 2 + (5 + 6) = \underline{\quad ? \quad}$

2. $16 \div 4 \times 2 = \underline{\quad ? \quad}$

3. $8 - 5 + 14 \div 2 = \underline{\quad ? \quad}$

4. $(3 + 4) \times (12 - 5) = \underline{\quad ? \quad}$

5. $4 + 20 \div 2 \times 3 = \underline{\quad ? \quad}$

6. $20 - (15 - 3) \div 2 = \underline{\quad ? \quad}$

Write the number that makes the number sentence true.

7. $7 + \boxed{} \times 2 = 17$

8. $2 \times (3 + \boxed{}) \div 4 = 6$

Write the operation symbol ($+$, $-$, $\times$, $\div$) that makes the number sentence true.

9. $15 \boxed{} 3 + 5 = 10$

10. $15 - (6 \boxed{} 2) + 11 = 18$

T R Y   I T

Place parentheses in the expression to make the number sentence true.

11. $7 + (5 \div 3) + 12 = 16$ **12.** $27 \div 9 \div 3 - 5 = 4$ **13.** $20 = 6 + (4 \times 2)$

Choose the answer.

14. $2 - (2 \times 1)$

   A. 0   B. 1   C. 2   D. 3

Read the problem and follow the directions.

15. Miraiah got the same answer when she solved $28 - 14 \div 2$ and $(28 - 14) \div 2$. Is she correct? Explain why or why not.
                                       21   7

16. Dallas got the same value for these two expressions. Is he correct? Explain why or why not.

- $8 \times (3 + 9)$
- $8 \times 3 + 9$

17. Derrick got the same value for these two expressions. Is he correct? Explain why or why not.

- $6 \times (3 - 3) + 1$
- $6 \times 3 - 3 + 1$

18. Frank got the same value for these two expressions. Is he correct? Explain why or why not.

- $(4 \times 6) + 4$
- $4 \times (6 + 4)$

19. Megan got the same value for these two expressions. Is she correct? Explain why or why not.

- $(9 \times 3) + (6 - 5)$
- $9 \times (3 + 6) - 5$

20. Richard and Cheryl solved these two equations:

- $8 \times 3 + 12 \div 4 = \underline{\ ?\ }$
- $8 \times (3 + 12) \div 4 = \underline{\ ?\ }$

Richard said the answer to both questions was 9. Cheryl said the answer to the first question was 27 and the answer to the second question was 30. Which student is correct? Explain the mistake that one of the students made.

21. Write an expression that is equal to 14 using only the numbers 2, 3, and 4.

TRY IT

The Distributive Property (A)

Evaluate Expressions

Write the missing number.

1. $2 \times (4 + 5) = 2 \times 4 + 2 \times \square$

2. $7 \times 5 - 7 \times 2 = 7 \times (\square - 2)$

3. $8 \times (9 - 3) = \square - 24$

4. $30 - 24 = \square \times (5 - 4)$

Use the distributive property or the order of operations to find the value of the expression in a different way.

5. $3 \times (6 - 3) = 3 \times 3 = 9$

6. $8 \times (4 + 6) = 32 + 48 = 80$

7. $5 \times (3 - 1) = 15 - 5 = 10$

8. $7 \times (8 + 4) = 7 \times 12 = 84$

Use the distributive property to multiply.

9. $56 \times 8 = (50 + 6) \times 8 = 50 \times 8 + 6 \times 8 = \square + \square = \square$

10. $7 \times 29 = 7 \times (30 - 1) = \underline{\ ?\ }$

11. $35 \times 6 = \underline{\ ?\ }$

Choose the answer.

12. Carla solved $6 \times (5 + 9)$ by saying the next step is 6×14. Which shows a different way to solve $6 \times (5 + 9)$?

    A. $5 + 9 \times 6$

    B. $6 \times 5 + 9$

    C. $6 \times 5 + 6 \times 9$

13. Which number replaces the box to make this a true sentence?
    $8 \times (2 + 5) = 16 + \square$

    A. 7

    B. 13

    C. 40

    D. 56

T R Y   I T

Write two number sentences that could be used to solve the problem.

14. Ellen is making 13 prize packages for her team mates. She is putting 6 bouncy balls and 3 barrettes into each package. What is the total number of objects she will put into the 13 packages?

15. Ken has 12 friends over. He gives each friend 5 stickers and 4 pencils when they leave. What is the total number of objects Ken gave to his 12 friends?

16. Coach Scott has 19 players on his team. He made each player a welcome bag. He put 5 baseballs and 2 batting gloves in each welcome bag. What is the total number of objects he put in the welcome bags?

Choose the two number sentences that could be used to solve the problem.

17. Ron has 14 friends at his party. He will give each friend 4 cars and 5 bouncy balls when they go home. What is the total number of toys he will give away?

    A. $14 \times (4 + 5) = \square$

    B. $14 \times 4 \times 5 = \square$

    C. $(14 \times 4) + (14 \times 5) = \square$

    D. $14 \times (4 \times 5) = \square$

18. Tim has a bucket for each of his 25 friends. Tim is going to put 12 shells in each bucket. How many shells does he need altogether?

    A. $25 + 12 = \square$

    B. $25 \times 12 = \square$

    C. $25 \times 10 + 25 \times 2 = \square$

    D. $25 \times 1 + 25 \times 2 = \square$

TRY IT

Story Problems: Solve and Check (A)

Choosing the Operation

To solve a story problem, you must first understand what the problem asks you to find. Then you have to decide which operation to use to find the answer. After you compute, you must look back to make sure your answer makes sense.

PROBLEM Identify the operation you would use to solve the problem. Then solve.

- Mr. Nichols works at the roller skating rink. He is replacing the wheels on the rental skates. He has 234 wheels. He puts 4 new wheels on each skate. How many skates will have all new wheels?

SOLUTION Division. Use the method that is easiest for you. One way is shown below.

1 You need to separate 234 wheels into equal groups of 4, so division is the best operation to use.

2 $234 \div 4 = 58$ r 2, or 58 skates with 2 wheels left over.

3 Read the problem again to decide which to do:

- Drop the remainder.
- Increase the quotient by 1.
- Express the remainder as a fraction.

4 The problem asks how many skates will have all new wheels. A skate must have 4 wheels, so 2 wheels are not enough for another skate. Drop the remainder. 58 skates will have all new wheels.

ANSWER division; 58 skates

LEARN

**Identify the operation you would use to solve the problem.
Then solve.**

1. Cody and Tyler launched model rockets. Tyler's rocket soared 1,418 feet. Cody's rocket reached a height 162 feet less than Tyler's rocket. How high, in feet, did did Cody's rocket fly?

2. Each year Bethlehem, Pennsylvania, hosts a music and arts festival called Musikfest. In 2006, there were 1,135,000 people at the festival. In 2008, 17,000 more people attended than in 2006. How many people attended Musikfest in 2008?

3. The veterans collected coats for their annual coat drive. Donated coats have come from 1,652 people in the community. Each person gave 4 coats. How many coats did the veterans collect in all?

4. The art council collected $56,218 in donations. The council used $32,187 to fund an art camp. How much money does the art council have left?

5. Sven works at the movie theater. He earns $8 an hour. He is saving money to buy a new bike. The bike costs $312. How many hours does Sven need to work to be able to buy the bike?

6. Cindy wore a pedometer to record the number of steps she walked in a day. She walked 9,784 steps. Each of her steps measures 2 feet long. How many total feet did Cindy walk in a day?

7. There were 287 customers at the photo shop in the morning. In the afternoon, 53 different customers entered the shop. How many total customers came to the photo shop that day?

40

L E A R N

Story Problems: Solve and Check (A)

Story Problems

Identify the operation you would use to solve the problem.
Then solve.

1. An empty plane weighs 176,650 pounds. The cargo and passengers weigh 117,280 pounds. What is the weight of the plane at takeoff?

2. An airplane can hold 255 passengers. On a flight from New York to Chicago, 32 seats are empty. How many passengers are on the plane?

3. Sam is building a model train display. He spends 4 hours each day working on it. He completes the display after 96 days. How many total hours did Sam spend building the display?

4. The bakery received an order for 182 blueberry muffins. The baker made the muffins and placed the muffins in boxes. Each box holds 6 muffins. How many boxes did the baker need to hold all the muffins?

Answer the question.

5. Small rose bushes cost $9 each. How many small rose bushes can Penny buy for $135?

6. A giraffe spends 20 hours a day grazing for food. How many hours would it spend grazing in 45 days?

7. Look back at Problem 4. How did the remainder affect your answer? Explain.

8. Fernando knows $6 \times 4 = 24$. How will this help him solve the problem $24 \div 6$?

9. The farmer planted some seeds with a machine. He planted 32 rows of seeds. Each row had 3,987 seeds. How many seeds did he plant?

Choose the answer.

10. The kitchen supply company made 2,987 bags of toothpicks. Each bag had 98 toothpicks. How many toothpicks did the company make altogether?

   A. 298,700   B. 292,726   C. 221,626   D. 197,476

11. Sharon solved this division problem. Which expression could be used to check her work?

$$4\overline{)2{,}794} \rightarrow 698\tfrac{2}{4}$$

   A. $(698 \times 2) + 4$ B. $(698 \times 4) + 2$

   C. $(698 + 2) \times 4$ D. $(698 + 4) \times 2$

TRY IT

Story Problems: Solve and Check (B)

Check the Answer

You can use the inverse operation to check a computation problem. Addition and subtraction are inverse operations. Multiplication and division are inverse operations.

PROBLEM Identify the operation you would use to check the answer. Then use that operation to decide if the answer is correct.
Write Yes if the answer is correct and No if the answer is not correct.

$$679 \div 6 = 113\frac{1}{6} \text{ or } 113 \text{ r } 1$$

SOLUTION

1 Since the problem is a division problem, its inverse operation is multiplication. To check it, you multiply and then add the remainder.

2 $113 \times 6 = 678$ and $678 + 1 = 679$

3
$$
\begin{array}{r}
113 \\
\times\ 6 \\
\hline
678 \\
+\ 1 \\
\hline
679
\end{array}
$$

4 Since $113 \times 6 + 1 = 679$, then the answer is correct.

ANSWER multiplication and then add the remainder; yes

Write the operation you would use to check the answer. Then use that operation to decide if the answer is correct. Write Yes if the answer is correct and No if the answer is not correct.

1.
$$
\begin{array}{r}
5{,}682 \\
+\ 739 \\
\hline
6{,}421
\end{array}
$$

2.
$$
\begin{array}{r}
259 \\
\times\ 8 \\
\hline
1{,}602
\end{array}
$$

3. $13{,}451 - 5{,}608 = 7{,}855$

4. $368 \div 5 = 73\frac{3}{5}$ or 73 r 3

LEARN

Write the operation you would use to check the solution to the story problem. Then use that operation to decide if the solution is correct. Write Yes if the solution is correct and No if the solution is not correct.

5. Each year, Bethlehem, Pennsylvania, hosts a music and art festival called Musikfest. In 2006, there were 1,135,000 people at the festival. In 2008, 17,000 more people than in 2006 attended the festival. How many people attended Musikfest in 2008?
1,152,000 people

6. Sven works at the movie theater. He earns $8 an hour. He is saving money to buy a new bike. The bike costs $312. How many hours does he need to work to be able to buy the bike?
39 hours

7. Cindy wore a pedometer to record the number of steps she walked in a day. She walked 9,784 steps. Each of her steps measures 2 feet long. How many total feet did she walk in a day?
19,488 feet

8. Mr. Nichols works at the roller skating rink. He is replacing the wheels on the rental skates. He has 234 wheels. He puts 4 new wheels on each skate. How many skates will have all new wheels?
$58\frac{2}{4}$, so 58 skates

Solve and check.

9. There are 1,572 books on each of 6 shelves at the library. How many books are there in all?

10. In a woodworking factory, craftsmen need to make 5,018 tables. Each craftsman can make 9 tables a day. How many craftsmen do they need to make all the tables in one day?

11. There are 450,486 sheets of card stock on the shelf at the office supply store. There are 23,115 more sheets of white paper than card stock. How many sheets of white paper are on the shelf?

12. There are 176,050 people living in the city where Pam lives. There are 150,280 fewer people living in the city where Craig lives than where Pam lives. How many people are living in the city where Craig lives?

LEARN

Story Problems: Solve and Check (B)

Is the Answer Correct?

Write the expression to use to check the answer.

1. $72 \times 8 = 576$
2. $3{,}613 - 154 = 3{,}459$
3. $753 \div 6 = 125\frac{3}{6}$

Read the problem and follow the directions.

4. The movie theater can seat a maximum of 562 people for each show. 15 shows had every seat filled. The manager thought a total of 8,420 people were at the movies. Is the manager correct? If not, write the correct answer.

5. City planners had lots of money in the bank. They took out $6,876 to pay for some trees. They had $3,543,987 left. How much money did they have in the beginning?

   Dave solved this problem and said the answer was $3,537,111. Is he correct? If not, write the correct answer.

6. The roof of an arena is made of tiles. There are 528,001 white tiles and 528,005 cream tiles. How many tiles are on the roof in all?

   Haley solved this problem and said the answer was 1,056,006. Is she correct? If not, write the correct answer.

7. The green turtle nests on Ascension Island. One year there were 14,765 turtle nests on the island. The next year there were 8,654 nests. How many fewer nests were there the second year?

   Julie solved this problem and said the answer was 6,111. Is she correct? If not, write the correct answer.

8. A music store has 16 pianos. Each piano has 88 keys. How many keys are there in all?

   Fred solved this problem and said the answer was 1,368. Is he correct? If not, write the correct answer.

9. A warehouse stored 3,624 cans of soup. The cans were divided equally on 8 shelves. How many cans of soup were on each shelf?

   Maria solved this problem and said the answer was 354. Is she correct? If not, write the correct answer.

TRY IT

Choose the answer.

10. Some fishermen caught 146,356 fish the first week and 218,406 fish the second week. How many more fish did they catch the second week than the first week? Colleen said the answer to this story problem is 72,150. Which equation could be used to check her answer?

    A. $72,150 + 146,356 = 218,406$
       Colleen is correct.

    B. $72,150 + 146,356 = 218,506$
       Colleen is not correct.

    C. $218,406 - 72,150 = 146,356$
       Colleen is correct.

    D. $72,150 - 146,356 = 74,206$
       Colleen is not correct.

11. A baker put 8 buns into each bag. He made 5,432 buns last month. How many bags did the baker use? Which equation will verify the correct answer to this story problem?

    A. $40,246 \div 8 = 5,432$
       He used 40,246 bags.

    B. $43,456 \div 8 = 5,432$
       He used 43,456 bags.

    C. $679 \times 8 = 5,432$
       He used 679 bags.

    D. $681 \times 8 = 5,432$
       He used 681 bags.

12. A humpback whale migrated 3,583 miles. It will travel another 1,517 miles to reach its feeding grounds. Richard said the whale will travel a total of 5,100 miles. Michael said the whale will travel a total of 4,090 miles. Which expression verifies the correct answer?

    A. $5,100 - 3,583$
       Richard is correct.

    B. $4,090 - 1,517$
       Michael is correct.

    C. $4,090 + 1,517$
       Michael is correct.

    D. $5,100 + 3,583$
       Richard is correct.

13. The airline owns 7 planes. Each plane can carry 343 passengers. What is the total number of passengers that can be on the planes at one time? Which equation can be used to check the answer to this story problem?

    A. $343 \div 7 = 49$
       There can be 49 passengers on the planes at one time.

    B. $343 \times 7 = 2,101$
       There can be 2,101 passengers on the planes at one time.

    C. $2,101 \div 7 = 343$
       There can be 2,101 passengers on the planes at one time.

    D. $2,401 \div 7 = 343$
       There can be 2,401 passengers on the planes at one time.

TRY IT

Rate Story Problems (A)

Solve Rate Story Problems

Solve.

1. Ward reads 6 books every month. At that rate, how many books does he read in a year?

2. Jana's softball team can run one lap around the field in 3 minutes. At that rate, how many minutes does it take the team to run 5 laps?

3. Dane has a bag of 220 chocolate chips. If he wants to have exactly 5 chips in each cookie, how many cookies can he make?

4. Sandy drives at a speed of 60 miles an hour. How many miles will she drive in 4 hours?

5. Marty drives at a speed of 55 miles an hour. How far will he drive in 3 hours?

6. How many seconds will it take Penny to walk 10,000 feet if she walks 4 feet every second?

7. Isa can finish a cartoon sketch in 4 minutes. If she sketches for 15 minutes, how many sketches will she finish?

Read the problem and write what you should do with the remainder.

8. Kara can knit a pair of socks in 2 days. At that rate, how many pairs of socks will she have finished in 15 days?

9. It takes Maria 1 minute to jog 3 city blocks. At that rate, how many minutes will she need to jog 70 city blocks?

TRY IT

Rate Story Problems (B)

Rate Problem Remainders

Worked Examples

Remainders in division problems affect the answers to story problems differently, depending on what a problem asks you to find. Before choosing your final answer, think carefully about what the story problem means.

PROBLEM A family is packing 26 large cans of spaghetti in boxes for a community service project. Each box holds 6 cans of food, or 6 cans per box. How many boxes must the family buy to hold the 26 cans?

$$
\begin{array}{r}
4 \\
6\overline{)26} \\
-24 \\
\hline
2
\end{array}
$$

SOLUTION

1 Ask yourself, "Should the remainder be expressed as a fraction?"

Think: The family cannot buy part of a box. Expressing the answer with a fraction, or $4\frac{2}{6}$, does not make sense. So the answer is not $4\frac{2}{6}$ boxes.

2 Ask yourself, "Should the remainder be dropped, so the answer is 4 boxes?"

Think: The family wants to send all 26 cans, but 4 boxes hold only 4×6, or 24, cans. So the answer is not 4 boxes.

3 Ask yourself, "Should the remainder make the quotient increase by 1, so the answer is 5 boxes?"

Think: The family needs the extra box to hold the last 2 cans. So the answer is 5 boxes.

ANSWER 5 boxes

L E A R N

Read the story problem. Study the division problem used to solve it. Choose the answer.

1. Mr. Robbins is building shelves for his son's model airplane collection. Each shelf must be 3 feet long. How many 3-foot shelves can Mr. Robbins make from a board that is 14 feet long?

$$\begin{array}{r} 4 \\ 3\overline{)14} \\ -12 \\ \hline 2 \end{array}$$

   A. 4 shelves

   B. 5 shelves

   C. $4\frac{2}{3}$ shelves

2. Nina had 33 inches of ribbon and made 5 award ribbons of equal length for the upcoming horse show. If Nina used all the ribbon, how long was each award ribbon, in inches?

$$\begin{array}{r} 6 \\ 5\overline{)33} \\ -30 \\ \hline 3 \end{array}$$

   A. 6 inches

   B. 7 inches

   C. $6\frac{3}{5}$ inches

3. A bench holds 5 soccer players, or 5 players per bench. If 17 soccer players need to sit on a bench before the game, how many benches does the coach need for the team?

$$\begin{array}{r} 3 \\ 5\overline{)17} \\ -15 \\ \hline 2 \end{array}$$

   A. 3 benches

   B. 4 benches

   C. $3\frac{2}{5}$ benches

4. Isaac can scan a photo in 2 minutes. At that rate, he scans photos for 11 minutes. How many photos will he finish scanning?

$$\begin{array}{r} 5 \\ 2\overline{)11} \\ -10 \\ \hline 1 \end{array}$$

   A. 5 photos

   B. 6 photos

   C. $5\frac{1}{2}$ photos

LEARN

Rate Story Problems (B)

Solve Rate Problems

Solve. Explain your answer.

1. Kim replaces her furnace filter every 8 weeks. In 770 weeks, how many times has she replaced the filter?

2. Springfield Zoo feeds the animals a total of 3,988 pounds of food each week. The zoo feeds the animals the same amount of food every day. How many pounds of food does the zoo feed in a day?

Solve.

3. A baseball player usually throws 83 pitches in 1 game. At that rate, how many pitches will he throw in 115 games?

4. Shelly's youth group bought 3 vans for $77,250. Each van costs the same amount. How much did the youth group pay for 1 van?

5. How many hours will it take Ian to drive 250 miles if he drives at a constant speed of 50 miles an hour?

6. How long will it take Bill to paint 70 feet of fence if he paints at a constant speed of 7 feet per hour?

7. Salt shakers cost $6 each. A cruise ship company paid $45,264 for salt shakers. How many salt shakers did the company buy?

8. Tennis balls cost $4 each. The tennis team paid $1,556 for tennis balls. How many tennis balls did the team buy?

9. Emily's printer prints 80 pages in 5 minutes. How many pages does the printer print in 1 minute?

10. Liliana bought 7 cartons of milk for $21. Each carton of milk was the same price. How much did she pay for 1 carton of milk?

11. Dora types 120 words in 6 minutes. If she types at a constant speed, how many words will she type each minute?

12. At Coyote Falls, 13,512 gallons of water go over the falls in 8 seconds. How many gallons of water go over the falls each second?

TRY IT

Fractions

Model Fractions

Write the fraction that the shaded part of the figure represents.

1. 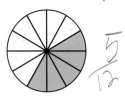 $\frac{4}{5}$

2. 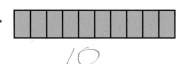 $\frac{10}{10}$

3.  $\frac{5}{12}$

4. 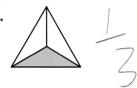 $\frac{1}{3}$

Write the fraction shown on the number line.

5. 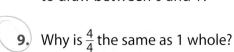 $\frac{6}{8}$

6. 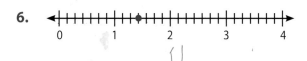 $\frac{11}{15}$

Answer the question.

7. Bobby wants to show $\frac{6}{11}$ on a number line. How many tick marks does he have to draw between 0 and 1?

8. Why is $\frac{5}{5}$ equal to 1 whole?

9. Why is $\frac{4}{4}$ the same as 1 whole?

Choose the answer.

10. Which shows $\frac{1}{4}$ shaded?

A.    B.   C.    D.

11. Which shows $\frac{8}{11}$ shaded?

A. 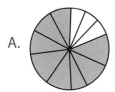 B.  C.   D.

12. Which shows the number $\frac{7}{8}$ on the number line?

A. 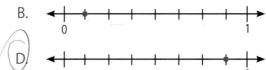   B.

0   1   0   1

C.   D.

0   1   0   1

13. Which explains how to show $\frac{5}{5}$?

A. Draw 10 circles, all the same size, and shade 5 of them.

B. Draw 5 triangles and 5 squares, and shade the 5 triangles.

C. Draw a rectangle divided into 5 equal parts, and shade 5 parts.

D. Draw a circle divided into 10 equal parts, and shade 5 parts.

14. Which explains how to show $\frac{9}{9}$?

A. Draw a square divided into 9 equal parts, and shade all 9 parts.

B. Draw 9 squares all the same shape and size, and shade 1 square.

C. Draw a circle with a 9 in the middle, and shade the circle.

D. Draw 9 squares all the same shape and size, and shade 1 square.

15. Melissa saw $\frac{6}{6}$ of the cake. Which statement is true?

A. Melissa saw 1 whole cake.

B. Melissa saw less than 1 whole cake.

C. Melissa saw more than 1 whole cake.

16. Which shows $\frac{2}{2}$ shaded?

A.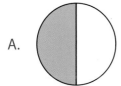

B.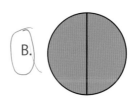

C.

D.

T R Y I T

Sketch Fractions

Draw Fractions

You can represent a fraction as a part of a whole, as a part of a set, or as a location on the number line.

PROBLEM Make three sketches to show $\frac{7}{12}$ as a part of a whole, as a part of a set, and as a location on a number line.

SOLUTION 1 $\frac{7}{12}$ as a part of a whole

The whole is divided into 12 equal sections. 7 of the sections are shaded.

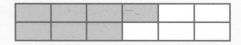

SOLUTION 2 $\frac{7}{12}$ as a part of a set

There are 12 objects in the set. 7 of the objects are circles.

SOLUTION 3 $\frac{7}{12}$ as a location on the number line

Each tick mark represents one-twelfth.

The point is on the 7th twelfth.

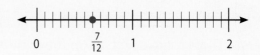

ANSWER

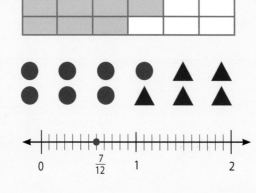

LEARN

Read the problem and follow the directions.

1. Make a sketch to represent $\frac{5}{6}$ as a part of a whole.

2. Make a sketch to represent $\frac{3}{7}$ as a part of a set.

3. Make a sketch to represent $\frac{4}{10}$ as a location on a number line.

4. Make a sketch to represent $\frac{10}{12}$.

5. Draw two rectangles that are the same size and shape. Divide one to show thirds. Divide one to show fifths. Which are larger, thirds or fifths? Use your drawings to explain.

Worked Examples

You can represent a mixed number more than one way.

PROBLEM 1 Sketch two rectangles and show that $\frac{6}{5}$ is the same as $1\frac{1}{5}$.

SOLUTION If $\frac{5}{5}$ equals 1 whole, then 6 fifths, or $\frac{6}{5}$, are shaded.
If $\frac{5}{5}$ equals 1 whole, then 1 whole and 1 fifth, or $1\frac{1}{5}$, are shaded.

ANSWER
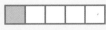
one whole

PROBLEM 2 Sketch two number lines and show that $\frac{26}{9}$ is the same as $2\frac{8}{9}$.

SOLUTION The point is located at $\frac{26}{9}$ as well as $2\frac{8}{9}$, so $\frac{26}{9}$ and $2\frac{8}{9}$ both name the same location on the number line, and $\frac{26}{9} = 2\frac{8}{9}$.

ANSWER
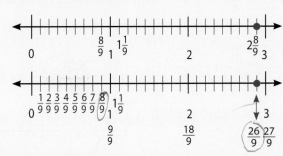

Read the problem and follow the directions.

6. Make a sketch that shows that $2\frac{2}{3} = \frac{8}{3}$.

Sketch Fractions

Fraction Sketches

Make a sketch to show the fraction.

1. $\frac{3}{4}$ as a part of a whole

2. $\frac{5}{7}$ as a part of a set

3. $\frac{1}{3}$ as a location on a number line

4. $3\frac{1}{4}$ as a part of a whole

5. $\frac{10}{12}$ as a part of a whole, as a part of a set, and as a location on a number line

Read the problem and follow the directions.

6. Put a dot on this number line to show the mixed number $3\frac{1}{4}$.

7. Shade $\frac{2}{6}$ of these objects.

8. Shade $\frac{1}{3}$ of these apples.

9. Shade $2\frac{4}{5}$ of these circles.

10. Draw 12 circles. Shade $\frac{5}{6}$ of them.

11. Shade $\frac{5}{7}$ of this rectangle.

12. Put a dot on this number line to show the number $\frac{7}{12}$.

TRY IT

Different Meanings of Fractions (A)

Fraction Meanings

Memory Jogger

Story Problem	Model	Fraction
Maggie walked $\frac{2}{4}$ mile on a straight road, stopped for a rest, and then walked $\frac{1}{4}$ mile farther. What fraction of a mile did Maggie walk in all?		$\frac{3}{4}$
Maggie has a container of 12 eggs. She cooks 8 eggs. What fraction of the eggs does Maggie cook?	OOOOOOOOOOOO	$\frac{8}{12}$
Maggie's house has 2 glass doors side-by-side. Each has 6 square panels. Maggie cleaned 6 of the panels in one door and 1 in the other door. What fraction of the doors did Maggie clean?		$1\frac{1}{6}$

Explain how the model shows the fraction.

1.  $\frac{4}{6}$

2.  $\frac{7}{9}$

Color 7

3. 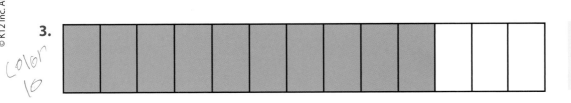 $\frac{10}{13}$

Color 10

T R Y   I T

Solve. Sketch the model.

4. Nick has a 3-foot-long measuring tape that is marked in inches.
He measures a board that is 1 foot, 5 inches long. One foot equals 12 inches.
What fraction explains the spot on the measuring tape that the board
reaches?

5. Leona made 8 cups of pudding. Her family ate 3 cups.
What fraction of the cups of pudding were left?

6. Six cousins were together for a family reunion.
Four of the cousins are girls. What fraction
represents the number of boys?

Choose the answer.

7. This image shows $\frac{3}{4}$ shaded.
Which other image shows the same fraction?

A.

B.

C.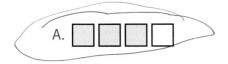

D.

8. This image shows $\frac{1}{3}$ shaded.
Which other image shows the same fraction?

A.

B.

C.

D.

9. This number line shows the fraction $\frac{2}{5}$.
Which other sketch shows the fraction $\frac{2}{5}$ shaded?

A.

B.

C.

D.

TRY IT

10. Which does **not** show $\frac{5}{6}$ shaded?

A.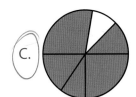

B.

C.

D.

11. Which does **not** show $\frac{4}{9}$ shaded?

A.    B.

C.    D.

12. Which shows $\frac{3}{8}$ on a number line?

A.    B.

C.    D.

13. Which shows $\frac{2}{5}$ on a number line?

A. 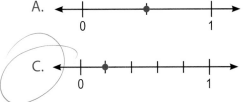   B.

C.   D.

T R Y   I T

14. Which shows $\frac{3}{4}$ on a number line?

A.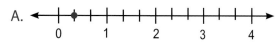

C.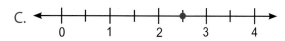

B.

D.

15. Which shows $2\frac{1}{3}$ on a number line?

A.

0   1   2   3   4

C.

0   1   2   3   4

B.

0   1   2   3   4

D.

0   1   2   3   4

16. Which shows $2\frac{1}{2}$ on a number line?

A.

0   1   2   3   4

C.

0   1   2   3   4

B.

0   1   2   3   4

D.

0   1   2   3   4

TRY IT

Different Meanings of Fractions (B)

Solve Fraction Problems

Solve.

1. A plumber needs to cut a 6-foot long pipe into 10 equal pieces. How long will each piece be?

2. Tony and Lisa equally share babysitting for a neighbor's child. If they babysit for 7 days in one week, how many days will each person babysit?

3. Karen bought 5 lemons and 7 oranges. What fraction of the fruit that she bought was oranges?

4. In New York City, there are 20 blocks in a mile. Tom walks 5 blocks from the train to his office every day. What part of a mile does he walk every day?

5. Emily bought 5 pounds of ground beef and divided it into 6 equal packages to freeze. How many pounds are in each package that Emily prepares?

6. Una cut a ribbon into 10 equal pieces. She sewed 7 pieces onto her quilt. What fraction of the ribbon did Una sew onto the quilt?

7. Sara lives 8 miles from her aunt's house. She rides her bike 6 miles and then stops to get a drink. What fraction of the trip to her aunt's house has Sara completed?

Choose the answer.

8. Which means the same as $\frac{3}{7}$?

   A. $\frac{1}{3} + \frac{1}{3} + \frac{1}{3} + \frac{1}{3} + \frac{1}{3} + \frac{1}{3} + \frac{1}{3}$

   B. $\frac{3}{3} + \frac{3}{3} + \frac{3}{3}$

   C. $\frac{1}{7} + \frac{1}{7} + \frac{1}{7}$

   D. $\frac{7}{7} + \frac{7}{7} + \frac{7}{7}$

9. Which means the same as $\frac{5}{4}$?

   A. $\frac{1}{5} + \frac{1}{5} + \frac{1}{5} + \frac{1}{5}$

   B. $\frac{5}{5} + \frac{5}{5} + \frac{5}{5} + \frac{5}{5}$

   C. $\frac{1}{4} + \frac{1}{4} + \frac{1}{4} + \frac{1}{4} + \frac{1}{4}$

   D. $\frac{4}{4} + \frac{4}{4} + \frac{4}{4} + \frac{4}{4} + \frac{4}{4}$

TRY IT

10. Which means the same as $2\frac{1}{4}$?

A. $\frac{1}{4}+\frac{1}{4}+\frac{1}{4}+\frac{1}{4}+\frac{1}{4}+\frac{1}{4}+\frac{1}{4}+\frac{1}{4}+\frac{1}{4}$

B. $\frac{1}{4}+\frac{1}{4}+\frac{1}{4}$

C. $\frac{1}{4}+\frac{1}{4}$

D. $\frac{2}{2}+\frac{2}{2}+\frac{2}{2}+\frac{2}{2}$

11. There are 10 balls in a bin, 7 yellow ones and 3 green ones.
What fraction of the balls is yellow?

A. $\frac{7}{3}$ B. $\frac{7}{10}$ C. $\frac{3}{7}$ D. $\frac{10}{7}$

12. Emil cut a log into 8 equal pieces. He burned 3 pieces in his fireplace.
Which number line shows the fraction of the log that was burned?

A.

B.

C.

D.

13. Suzanne cut a ribbon into 9 equal pieces. She sewed 5 pieces onto her quilt.
Which number line shows the fraction of the ribbon that was sewn onto the quilt?

A.

B.

C.

D.

Different Meanings of Fractions (C)

Fractions as Ratios

Worked Examples

Fractions can show a *ratio*, or a comparison between two amounts. The order in which you are asked to compare amounts is important. The first amount in a ratio is the numerator. The second amount in a ratio is the denominator.

PROBLEM 1 Compare the length of the red segment to the length of the black segment. Then explain their relationship. Next express the ratio of the red to the black as a fraction.

SOLUTION

1 Trace the shorter segment. Cut it out.

2 Compare the length of the red segment to the black segment.

3 4 red segments = 1 black segment ⟵——————— Count as you measure.

4 The length of the red segment is ⟵——————— Write a comparison sentence.
$\frac{1}{4}$ of the length of the black segment.

5 The ratio of red to black is $\frac{1}{4}$. ⟵——— Write the ratio of red to black as a fraction.

ANSWER The length of the red segment is $\frac{1}{4}$ of the length of the black segment.
The ratio of red to black is $\frac{1}{4}$.

L E A R N

PROBLEM 2 Compare the length of the red segment to the length of the black segment. Then explain their relationship. Next express the ratio of the red to the black as a fraction.

SOLUTION

1 Trace the shorter segment. Cut it out.

2 Compare the length of the red segment to the length of the black segment.

3 1 red segment = 5 black segments ⟵————————— Count as you measure.

4 The red segment is 5 times the ⟵————— Write a comparison sentence.
length of the black segment.

5 The ratio of red to black is $\frac{5}{1}$. ⟵——— Write the ratio of red to black as a fraction.

ANSWER The length of the red segment is 5 times the length of the black segment. The ratio of red to black is $\frac{5}{1}$.

Compare the length of the red segment to the length of the black segment. Then explain their relationship. Next express the ratio as a fraction.

1.

2.

3.

4.

5.

6.

7.

Different Meanings of Fractions (C)

Write Fractions to Compare

Solve.

1. The line segments below show the lengths of a baby's shoe and an adult's shoe. What fraction can you use to compare the length of the baby's shoe to the length of the adult's shoe?

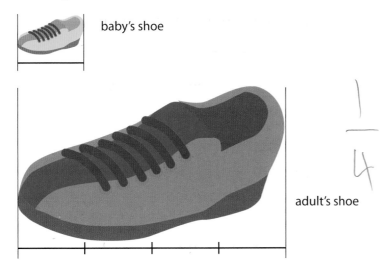

baby's shoe

adult's shoe

$$\frac{1}{4}$$

2. What fraction can you write to compare line segment *A* to line segment *B*?

$$\frac{3}{5}$$

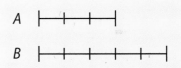

3. Caroline is 16 years old and Jim is 12 years old. What fraction compares Caroline's age to Jim's age?

$$\frac{16}{12}$$

4. What fraction can you write to compare line segment *A* to line segment *B*?

$$\frac{1}{3}$$

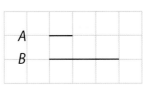

5. Sam's hand measures 5 inches and his arm measures 16 inches. Write a fraction to compare the length of Sam's hand to the length of his arm.

$$\frac{5}{16}$$

TRY IT

6. How many of line segment *C* does it take to measure line segment *D*?

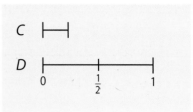

Write a fraction to compare the length of line segment *C* to line segment *D*.

Write a fraction to compare the length of line segment *D* to line segment *C*.

7. Hank had 3 pounds of hamburger meat and 4 pounds of hot dogs. What fraction tells the fraction of the pounds of hot dogs Hank had to the pounds of hamburger meat?

$$\frac{4}{3}$$

8. Marie had 12 pears in a bowl. She and her friends ate 5 pears. What fraction of the pears are left in the bowl?

$$\frac{5}{12}$$

9. Tanya is 2. Her brother is 5. What fraction represents Tanya's age compared to her brother's age?

$$\frac{2}{5}$$

10. Helen is 8. Her cousin is 12. What fraction represents Helen's age compared to her cousin's age?

$$\frac{8}{12}$$

Choose the answer.

11. Jacques cut a cucumber into 7 equal pieces. He ate 3 pieces. Which shows the fraction of the cucumber that was left?

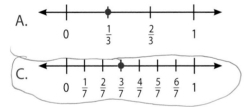

12. There were 10 ducks in the water. Three of the ducks got out of the water. Which shows the fraction of the ducks that are left in the water?

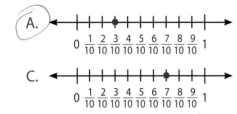
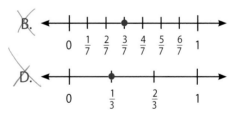

T R Y I T

13. Dave had 9 library books. He returned 7 of them to the library. Which shows the fraction of the library books that he still has?

A.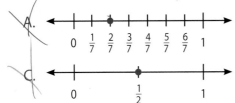

B.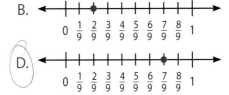

C.

0          $\frac{1}{2}$ 1

D.

0 $\frac{1}{9}$ $\frac{2}{9}$ $\frac{3}{9}$ $\frac{4}{9}$ $\frac{5}{9}$ $\frac{6}{9}$ $\frac{7}{9}$ $\frac{8}{9}$ 1

14. Willa is 3. Her brother is 8. Which fraction represents Willa's age compared to her brother's age?

A. $\frac{3}{8}$

B. $\frac{5}{8}$

C. $\frac{3}{11}$

D. $\frac{8}{11}$

15. Saul has 2 bottles that he could use for his juice. One bottle holds 8 ounces. The other bottle holds 12 ounces. Which fraction represents how much the smaller bottle holds compared to the larger bottle?

A. $\frac{12}{8}$

B. $\frac{8}{20}$

C. $\frac{12}{20}$

D. $\frac{8}{12}$

16. Manny has a piece of ribbon that is 11 inches long. He wants to cut a piece that is 7 inches long for a decoration. Which fraction represents how long the piece for the decoration will be compared to the length of ribbon?

A. $\frac{6}{11}$

B. $\frac{7}{11}$

C. $\frac{11}{18}$

D. $\frac{7}{18}$

TRY IT

Explain Equivalent Fractions (A)

Show Equivalent Fractions

Explain how the pictures show that the fractions are equivalent.

1. $\frac{3}{4} = \frac{6}{8}$

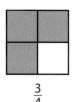

$\frac{3}{4}$ $\frac{6}{8}$

half of 6 is 3 and half or 8 is 4 soy they are equivalent the same

2. $\frac{1}{2} = \frac{4}{8}$

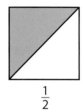

$\frac{1}{2}$ $\frac{4}{8}$

Tell whether the pair of fractions are equivalent.
Answer Yes or No, and explain your answer.

3. $\frac{2}{6}$ and $\frac{1}{3}$ *Yes*

4. $\frac{4}{10}$ and $\frac{2}{5}$ *Yes*

Answer the question. Then explain how you can make a sketch or draw a number line to answer the question.

5. Are the fractions $\frac{2}{4}$ and $\frac{4}{8}$ equivalent?   *Yes*

6. Are the fractions $\frac{2}{4}$ and $\frac{1}{2}$ equivalent?   *Yes*

7. Are the fractions $\frac{5}{6}$ and $\frac{2}{3}$ equivalent?   *No*

8. Are the fractions $\frac{6}{10}$ and $\frac{3}{5}$ equivalent?   *Yes*

9. Are the fractions $\frac{2}{6}$ and $\frac{3}{9}$ equivalent?   *No*

TRY IT

Explain Equivalent Fractions (B)

Equivalent or Not?

Use the number line to find four fractions that are equivalent to $\frac{1}{2}$.

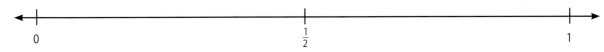

1.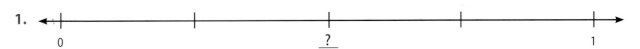

2.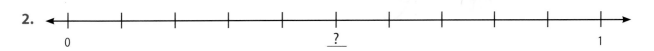

3.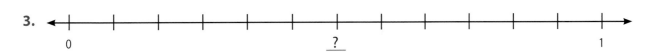

4.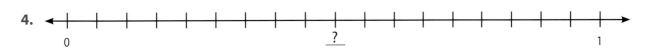

Use the number line to find three fractions that are equivalent to $\frac{1}{3}$.

5.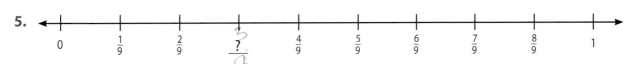

6.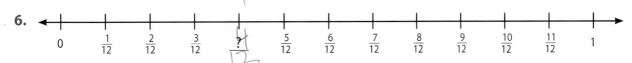

7.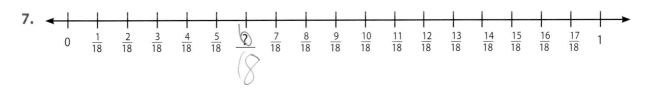

TRY IT

Answer the question. Then explain how you can make a sketch or draw a number line to answer the question.

8. Are the fractions $\frac{4}{6}$ and $\frac{8}{12}$ equivalent?

   yes

9. Are the fractions $1\frac{2}{3}$ and $1\frac{2}{6}$ equivalent?

   No

10. Are the fractions $2\frac{1}{2}$ and $2\frac{5}{8}$ equivalent?

   No

11. Are the fractions $\frac{6}{3}$ and $\frac{12}{2}$ equivalent?

   No

12. Are the fractions $\frac{12}{5}$ and $\frac{24}{10}$ equivalent?

   maybe

TRY IT

Find a Fraction (A)

Where's the Fraction?

Use the number lines to find a fraction between the two given numbers.
There may be more than one possible answer.

1. 0 and $\frac{3}{8}$

2. $\frac{1}{2}$ and 1

3. $\frac{1}{4}$ and $\frac{5}{8}$

Choose which fraction lies between the two given numbers. Use the
number line printouts to help you, although some number pairs may not
appear on the printouts.

4. $\frac{1}{2}$ and 1

    A. $\frac{3}{4}$ B. $\frac{1}{8}$ C. $\frac{1}{4}$ D. $\frac{3}{8}$

5. 0 and $\frac{1}{2}$

    A. $\frac{5}{8}$ B. $\frac{3}{8}$ C. $\frac{3}{4}$ D. $\frac{7}{8}$

6. $\frac{1}{2}$ and $\frac{7}{8}$

    A. $\frac{1}{8}$ B. $\frac{3}{4}$ C. $\frac{4}{8}$ D. $\frac{7}{2}$

7. 0 and $\frac{1}{2}$

    A. $\frac{8}{12}$ B. $\frac{7}{8}$ C. $\frac{1}{4}$ D. $\frac{5}{6}$

TRY IT

8. $\frac{1}{2}$ and 1

    A. $\frac{1}{12}$ B. $\frac{3}{5}$ C. $\frac{1}{4}$ D. $\frac{3}{12}$

9. 1 and 2

    A. $\frac{1}{2}$ B. $2\frac{1}{2}$ C. $2\frac{1}{4}$ D. $1\frac{2}{3}$

10. $1\frac{1}{2}$ and 2

    A. $1\frac{7}{8}$ B. $1\frac{1}{10}$ C. $\frac{8}{9}$ D. $2\frac{1}{11}$

11. 2 and $2\frac{1}{2}$

    A. $2\frac{2}{5}$ B. $2\frac{4}{5}$ C. $3\frac{1}{2}$ D. $1\frac{8}{9}$

12. 3 and 4

    A. $2\frac{3}{5}$ B. $1\frac{3}{6}$ C. $4\frac{1}{4}$ D. $3\frac{5}{8}$

13. 3 and $3\frac{1}{2}$

    A. $2\frac{6}{7}$ B. $3\frac{4}{5}$ C. $3\frac{1}{4}$ D. $4\frac{1}{2}$

14. 4 and 5

    A. $3\frac{3}{4}$ B. $4\frac{1}{5}$ C. $5\frac{2}{4}$ D. $3\frac{1}{3}$

15. 4 and $4\frac{1}{2}$

    A. $4\frac{2}{5}$ B. $4\frac{3}{4}$ C. $4\frac{7}{8}$ D. $5\frac{1}{3}$

16. $4\frac{1}{2}$ and 5

    A. $5\frac{1}{8}$ B. $4\frac{5}{8}$ C. $4\frac{1}{3}$ D. $3\frac{10}{11}$

TRY IT

Find a Fraction (B)

Find Fractions and Mixed Numbers

Use the number lines to find a fraction between each given pair of numbers.
There may be more than one possible answer.

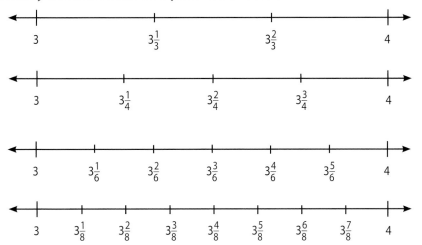

1. $3\frac{2}{3}$ and $3\frac{5}{6}$

2. $3\frac{1}{8}$ and $3\frac{3}{4}$

Use the number line printouts to find and write **two** fractions that lie between the two given numbers.

3. 0 and $\frac{4}{8}$

4. $4\frac{3}{6}$ and 5

Choose which fraction lies between the two given numbers.
Use the number line printouts to help you, although some number pairs may not appear on the printouts.

5. 0 and $\frac{1}{2}$

A. $\frac{4}{8}$

B. $\frac{2}{3}$

C. $\frac{3}{4}$

D. $\frac{1}{6}$

6. $1\frac{2}{3}$ and 2

A. $1\frac{1}{8}$

B. $1\frac{7}{9}$

C. $1\frac{4}{8}$

D. $1\frac{3}{5}$

7. 0 and $\frac{2}{4}$

    A. $\frac{3}{4}$ B. $\frac{5}{6}$ C. $\frac{7}{8}$ D. $\frac{1}{8}$

8. $\frac{6}{12}$ and 1

    A. $\frac{3}{8}$ B. $\frac{7}{10}$ C. $\frac{1}{6}$ D. $\frac{2}{5}$

9. $1\frac{1}{3}$ and 2

    A. $1\frac{1}{6}$ B. $1\frac{4}{9}$ C. $1\frac{1}{8}$ D. $1\frac{1}{9}$

10. $4\frac{1}{3}$ and 5

    A. $4\frac{4}{9}$ B. $4\frac{1}{6}$ C. $4\frac{1}{8}$ D. $4\frac{1}{9}$

TRY IT

Estimate Lengths

Estimate Line Segments

Worked Examples

You can refer to a dual-scale ruler to estimate line segments.

PROBLEM Estimate the length of the line segment to the nearest inch and to the nearest centimeter.

SOLUTION

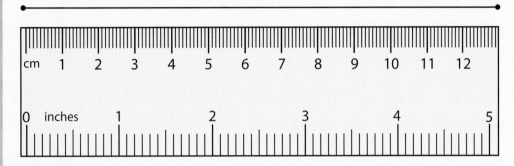

ANSWER about 5 in., about 13 cm

Estimate the length of the line segment to the nearest inch and to the nearest centimeter.

1. •————————————•

2. •————————————————•

3. •————•

4. •————————•

LEARN

Answer the question.

5. What is the length of the pencil in inches?

6. What is the length of the pencil in centimeters?

LEARN

Estimate Lengths

Length Estimation

Estimate the length of the object to the nearest inch.

1.

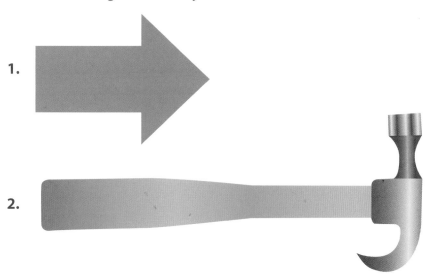

2.

Estimate the length of the object to the nearest centimeter.

3.

4.

Choose the answer.

5. Which is closest to 1 inch long?

   A. banana   B. spoon

   C. fork   D. grape

6. Which is closest to 1 centimeter long?

   A. raisin   B. lamp

   C. baseball bat   D. piano bench

TRY IT

Measurement in Story Problems (A)

Nature Story Problems

Worked Examples

To solve this story problem, read the problem, answer questions about the problem, and then solve the problem.

PROBLEM   A thirsty Asian elephant can drink 59 gallons of water.

How many gallons can 3 thirsty Asian elephants drink?

What operation can you use?

What number sentence can you use to solve the problem?

SOLUTION   You know 1 Asian elephant can drink 59 gallons of water. To find how many gallons 3 Asian elephants can drink, you *multiply*.

$3 \times 59 = ?$

ANSWER   multiply; $3 \times 59 = ?$; 177 gallons

Read the problem, answer the questions about the problem, and then solve the problem.

1. Baby camels, called calves, grow to full size in about 6 years. Suppose 5 adult camels weigh 2,500 kilograms altogether and they each weigh the same amount.

    How much does 1 camel weigh?

    What operation can you use?

    What number sentence can you use to solve the problem?

LEARN

Solve.

2. A blue whale calf can drink 128 gallons of milk per day.
There are 4 quarts in 1 gallon.

   How many quarts of milk are in 128 gallons?

   How many quarts of milk can 3 blue whale calves drink in one day?

3. Adult humpback whales can eat 3,000 pounds of food a day.

   How many pounds of food can 12 humpback whales
   eat in a day?

   There are 16 ounces in 1 pound. How many ounces of food
   can 1 humpback whale eat in a day?

4. A line of ants is 980 millimeters long. If each ant is 7 millimeters long,
   how many ants are in the line?

5. Carpenter ants live outside in mountains as high as 9,000 feet.
   There are 3 feet in 1 yard. How many yards are in 9,000 feet?

Measurement in Story Problems (A)

Using Equal Measures

Solve.

1. Matt has 96 pounds of dog food. He stores the food in 6-pound containers. How many containers will he need?

2. Sound travels about 1,000 feet in 1 second. About how far will the noise from thunder travel in 5 seconds?

3. A store has 220 yards of checked fabric that sells for $11 a yard. If the store sells all of the checked fabric, how much money will the store take in?

4. Justine made 2,000 milliliters of chicken soup. She divides it into 8 equal portions. How many milliliters are in each portion of soup?

5. A bald eagle can eat 3,850 grams of fish in a week, or 7 days. If the eagle eats the same amount each day, how many grams of fish will the eagle eat in a day?

Choose the answer.

6. Kevin charged $6 to wash a car. He washed 12 cars. How much money did he earn?

    A. $94   B. $72   C. $18   D. $2

7. Thirty cyclists each drank 2 pints of water. How many pints of water did they drink altogether?

    A. 90 pints   B. 60 pints   C. 30 pints   D. 15 pints

8. Picture frames cost $9 each. How many picture frames can Eric buy for $135?

    A. 1,215   B. 675   C. 15   D. 2

9. Lyn spent $54 for 9 plants for her backyard. If each plant costs the same amount, how much did each plant cost?

    A. $6   B. $8   C. $456   D. $486

TRY IT

Measurement in Story Problems (B)

Everyday Measurements

Worked Examples

You can multiply or divide to solve story problems with equal measures. The operation you choose depends on what the problem asks you to find.

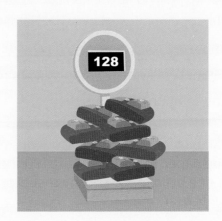

PROBLEM A group of 8 hikers wore backpacks of equal weight. The backpacks had a total weight of 128 pounds.

What was the weight of each backpack?

SOLUTION

Do you know the total, or do you have to find it? $\longrightarrow$ I know the total.

What operation will you use to solve the problem? $\longrightarrow$ division

What is the solution to the problem? $\longrightarrow$ 128 total pounds (lb) ÷ 8 hikers = 16 pounds (lb) per backpack

ANSWER 16 pounds (lb)

Solve.

1. A large can of tomato soup weighs 538 grams. What is the weight of 2 cans of soup?

   Do you know the total, or do you have to find it?

   What operation will you use to solve?

   What is the solution to the problem?

L E A R N

2. Tony's train layout has 216 inches of straight track. The track comes in 9-inch sections. How many sections of straight track does Tony's layout have?

   Do you know the total, or do you have to find it?

   What operation will you use to solve the problem?

   What is the solution to the problem?

3. Natalie ran in a 5-mile race. One mile equals 5,280 feet. What is the total number of feet that Natalie ran?

   Do you know the total, or do you have to find it?

   What operation will you use to solve the problem?

   What is the solution to the problem?

4. At a hot-air balloon festival, 300 students make hot-air balloons from tissue paper. Each student uses 30 sheets of colored tissue paper for one balloon. How many sheets of tissue paper will the students use?

   Do you know the total, or do you have to find it?

   What operation will you use to solve the problem?

   What is the solution to the problem?

5. A popular entertainment show had 4 contestants. Viewers called in 48,400 votes in all. If each contestant received the same number of votes, how many votes did each contestant receive?

   Do you know the total, or do you have to find it?

   What operation will you use to solve the problem?

   What is the solution to the problem?

6. Juan recycles the ink cartridges from his computer printer. He gets a $3 coupon for each recycled cartridge. Juan received $189 worth of coupons in two years. How many cartridges did he recycle in that time?

   Do you know the total, or do you have to find it?

   What operation will you use to solve the problem?

   What is the solution to the problem?

LEARN

Measurement in Story Problems (B)

Equal Measures

Solve.

1. A telephone worker has 1,407 feet of telephone wire. He completes 7 jobs and uses the same amount of wire for each job.

   How many feet of wire does the telephone worker use for each job?

2. A bottle of shampoo holds 945 milliliters. Grace uses 3 milliliters of shampoo each time she washes her hair.

   How many times can Grace wash her hair before the shampoo runs out?

3. The hockey team wants to buy sew-on patches for the players. The patches cost $5 each.

   How many patches can the team buy if it spends $150?

4. John spent $250 for 5 new lawn chairs.

   If each chair costs the same amount, how much did each chair cost?

Choose the answer.

5. Ethan is placing tiles along the edge of a countertop. Each tile is 8 centimeters long.

   How many tiles will Ethan need if the countertop is 144 centimeters long?

   A. 18 tiles

   B. 12 tiles

   C. 18 centimeters

   D. 1,152 centimeters

6. Joe's company bought 48 golf umbrellas with the company logo.

   If each umbrella cost $16, how much did Joe's company spend on them?

   A. $3

   B. $4

   C. $640

   D. $768

7. Animated movies on DVD are on sale for $9 each. Alexis has $135 to spend.

   How many DVDs can Alexis buy?

   A. 15 DVDs

   B. 19 DVDs

   C. $15

   D. 1,215 DVDs

8. Michelle has 8 kites. She used 64 feet of string on each kite.

   How much string did Michelle use on all 8 kites?

   A. 8 feet

   B. 512 feet

   C. 504 feet

   D. 612 feet

TRY IT

Measure Temperature

Temperature and Tools

Worked Examples

Temperature describes how hot or cold something is. We can use a thermometer to measure temperature in degrees Fahrenheit (°F) or in degrees Celsius (°C).

PROBLEM Use the Celsius thermometer to answer the questions. What temperature does the thermometer show? Is this temperature the boiling point of water, the freezing point of water, normal body temperature, or room temperature?

SOLUTION

1 Use a sheet of paper to line up the top of the mercury with the thermometer to its left. Notice that each tick mark represents 1 degree on this thermometer. Count the tick marks above 30°C. There are 7 tick marks, so the thermometer shows 37°C.

2 You know that 0°C is the freezing point, 100°C is the boiling point, and 21°C is about room temperature. Since 37°C is much higher than room temperature, it must be the normal body temperature.

ANSWER 37°C; normal body temperature

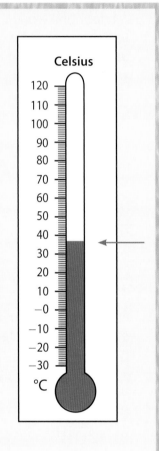

LEARN

Answer the question. Use the Fahrenheit thermometer shown here. Notice that each tick mark represents 2 degrees on this thermometer.

1. At what temperature does water boil?

2. What is a comfortable room temperature?

3. At what temperature does water freeze?

4. What is the temperature on a very cold day?

5. About what reading is normal body temperature?

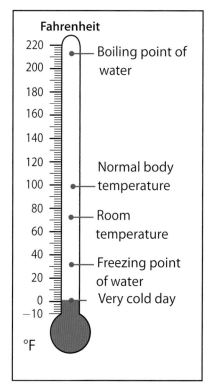

Answer the question. Use the Celsius thermometer shown here.

6. What is a comfortable room temperature?

7. At what temperature does water freeze?

8. About what reading is normal body temperature?

9. What is the temperature on a very cold day?

10. At what temperature does water boil?

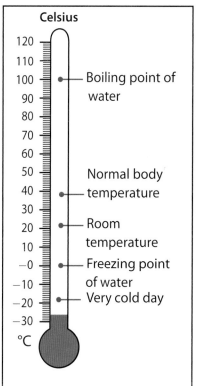

L E A R N

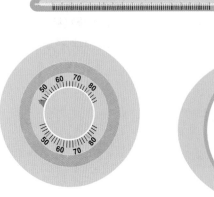
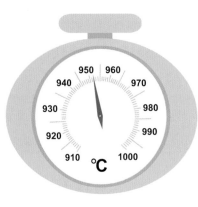

Read the problem and follow the directions.

11. Find and list the kinds of thermometers you have in and around your home.

Choose the answer.

12. Which thermometer shows the temperature inside a refrigerator in the metric system?

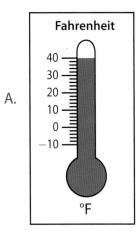
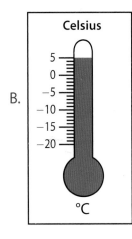

13. Which thermometer shows the outdoor temperature on a hot day by using the English, or customary, system?

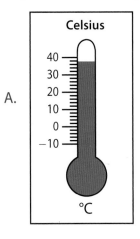
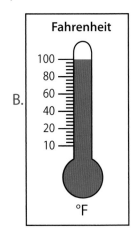

14. Which is a temperature measurement in degrees Celsius?

    A. 55°C   B. 55°F

    C. 55 m   D. 55 L

15. Which is a temperature measurement in degrees Fahrenheit?

    A. 38 in.   B. 38 sec

    C. 38 pt   D. 38°F

16. Which tool would you use to measure body temperature?

A.
B.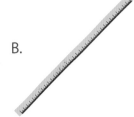
C.
D.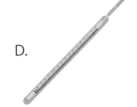

L E A R N

Measure Temperature

Tell the Temperature

Answer the question. Use the Celsius thermometer shown.
Pay close attention to the scale that the thermometer uses.

1. The oven in the science lab was being used to melt and purify iron. What was the temperature of the oven? Notice that each tick mark represents 10 degrees on this thermometer.

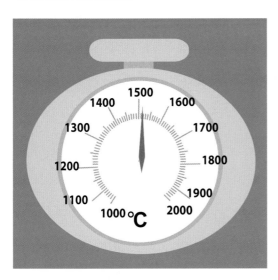

2. Hillary looked at the thermometer outside her window one day last winter. What was the temperature outside? Notice that each tick mark represents 1 degree on this thermometer.

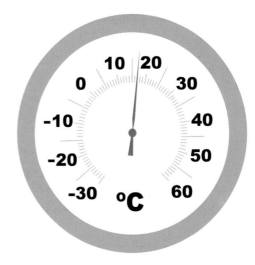

Choose the answer.

3. Alyssa said that water freezes at 32. Which unit should she use?

   A. °F   B. °C

   C. °M   D. °T

4. The weather was warm and breezy. The weather report stated that the high for the city would be 78. Which unit should be used?

   A. °T   B. °F

   C. °C   D. °M

5. Lisa said to preheat the oven to 375. Which unit should she use?

   A. °M   B. °T

   C. °F   D. °C

6. Which is the metric unit for measuring temperature?

   A. °M   B. °F

   C. °C   D. °T

TRY IT

7. Ann Marie said that gold melts at a temperature of approximately 1,064. Which unit should she use?

A. °C

B. °T

C. °M

D. °G

8. Alex said that copper melts at a temperature of approximately 1,083. Which unit should he use?

A. °M

B. °C

C. °T

D. °G

9. Ismael used his mom's candy thermometer to check the temperature of the sugar and water mixture. What was the temperature?

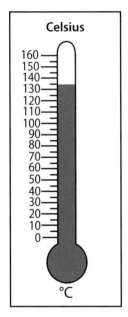

A. 130°C

B. 135°C

C. 140°C

D. 145°C

10. The oven that is used to melt bronze at the statue shop beeps when the bronze is melting. What is the temperature of the oven?

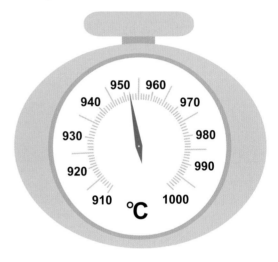

A. 948°C

B. 949°C

C. 951°C

D. 952°C

TRY IT

Add and Subtract Fractions (A)

Add, Subtract, and Simplify

Worked Examples

You can use fraction strips to add, subtract, and simplify fractions.

PROBLEM 1 You need $\frac{1}{6}$ cup milk to make one recipe. You need $\frac{3}{6}$ cup to make another recipe. How much milk do you need to make both recipes? Use fraction strips to find the sum in simplest form. Then write the problem and show your work.

SOLUTION

1 Begin with 1 one-sixth piece on the fraction strip.

$\frac{1}{6}$	$\frac{1}{6}$	$\frac{1}{6}$	$\frac{1}{6}$	$\frac{1}{6}$	$\frac{1}{6}$

2 Add 3 one-sixth pieces to the 1 one-sixth piece. There are 4 one-sixth pieces, so $\frac{1}{6} + \frac{3}{6} = \frac{4}{6}$.

$\frac{1}{6}$	$\frac{1}{6}$	$\frac{1}{6}$	$\frac{1}{6}$	$\frac{1}{6}$	$\frac{1}{6}$

3 Simplify the sum if possible. Look for one fraction piece or two or more identical pieces that are each larger than a one-sixth piece but combine to be the same length as $\frac{4}{6}$. A strip with 2 one-third pieces is the same length as 4 one-sixth pieces, so $\frac{4}{6} = \frac{2}{3}$.

$\frac{1}{3}$	$\frac{1}{3}$	$\frac{1}{3}$

$$
\begin{array}{r}
\frac{1}{6} \\
+ \;\frac{3}{6} \\
\hline
\frac{4}{6} = \frac{2}{3}
\end{array}
$$

ANSWER You need $\frac{2}{3}$ cup milk to make both recipes.

L E A R N

PROBLEM 2 A black tropical fish is $\frac{5}{8}$ inch long. A yellow tropical fish is $\frac{3}{8}$ inch long. How much longer is the black tropical fish than the yellow tropical fish?

Use fraction strips to find the difference in simplest form. Then write the problem and show your work.

SOLUTION

1 Begin with 5 one-eighth pieces on the fraction strip. Place 3 one-eighth pieces below the 5 pieces. Compare the shaded parts of the fraction strips.

| $\frac{1}{8}$ | $\frac{1}{8}$ | $\frac{1}{8}$ | $\frac{1}{8}$ | $\frac{1}{8}$ | $\frac{1}{8}$ | $\frac{1}{8}$ | $\frac{1}{8}$ |

| $\frac{1}{8}$ | $\frac{1}{8}$ | $\frac{1}{8}$ | $\frac{1}{8}$ | $\frac{1}{8}$ | $\frac{1}{8}$ | $\frac{1}{8}$ | $\frac{1}{8}$ |

2 Subtract by comparing $\frac{5}{8}$ to $\frac{3}{8}$ or take away 3 matching pairs of one-eighth pieces. The difference, or $\frac{2}{8}$, is left.

3 Simplify the difference if possible. Because 1 one-fourth piece is the same length as 2 one-eighth pieces, the fraction $\frac{1}{4}$ equals $\frac{2}{8}$.

| $\frac{1}{8}$ | $\frac{1}{8}$ | $\frac{1}{8}$ | $\frac{1}{8}$ | $\frac{1}{8}$ | $\frac{1}{8}$ | $\frac{1}{8}$ | $\frac{1}{8}$ |

| $\frac{1}{4}$ | $\frac{1}{4}$ | $\frac{1}{4}$ | $\frac{1}{4}$ |

ANSWER The black tropical fish is $\frac{1}{4}$ inch longer than the yellow tropical fish.

$$\begin{array}{r} \frac{5}{8} \\ -\ \frac{3}{8} \\ \hline \frac{2}{8} = \frac{1}{4} \end{array}$$

Use fraction strips to write the fraction in simplest form.

1. $\frac{4}{8}$ 2. $\frac{2}{6}$ 3. $\frac{4}{12}$ 4. $\frac{2}{10}$

Solve. Use fraction strips to add or subtract. Write the answer in simplest form.

5. Toby and his father walk $\frac{1}{2}$ mile to the store. Then they walk $\frac{1}{6}$ mile to the library.

How far do they walk in all?

LEARN

6. John prints a program for the community theater play. The text takes up $\frac{2}{3}$ of the page. The art takes up $\frac{1}{6}$ of the page.

   How much of the page has text or art?

7. Maria has $\frac{3}{4}$ yard of fabric. She cuts $\frac{2}{4}$ yard and uses it for a craft.

   How much of the fabric is left?

8. Molly mixes trail mix and raisins to make a snack. She makes $\frac{5}{6}$ cup of the snack. She uses $\frac{2}{3}$ cup trail mix.

   How many cups of raisins does Molly use?

LEARN

Add and Subtract Fractions (A)

Use Sketches to Add and Subtract

Worked Examples

You can make sketches to help you solve story problems that involve addition and subtraction of fractions.

PROBLEM 1 Joshua has a board that is $\frac{3}{4}$ yard long. He cuts off $\frac{1}{4}$ yard. How long is the board now? Sketch pictures on grid paper to find the difference.

SOLUTION

1 Sketch a rectangle to show $\frac{3}{4}$.

Below that rectangle, sketch another rectangle the same size that shows $\frac{1}{4}$.

2 Compare the shaded parts of the grids to subtract.

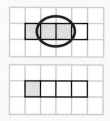

$\frac{3}{4}$ is $\frac{2}{4}$ longer than $\frac{1}{4}$, so $\frac{3}{4} - \frac{1}{4} = \frac{2}{4}$.

3 Decide if you can simplify $\frac{2}{4}$. Sketch $\frac{2}{4}$ on a new rectangle and sketch a blank rectangle the same size below it. Try to find a fraction larger than $\frac{1}{4}$ that is the same length as $\frac{2}{4}$ and shade it. Since $\frac{2}{4}$ and $\frac{1}{2}$ cover the same fraction of the rectangle, $\frac{2}{4}$ in simplest form is $\frac{1}{2}$.

4 Show your work and write the solution.

$$\begin{array}{r} \frac{3}{4} \\ - \ \frac{1}{4} \\ \hline \frac{2}{4} = \frac{1}{2} \end{array}$$

ANSWER The board is $\frac{1}{2}$ yard long.

L E A R N

PROBLEM 2 Gia read $\frac{1}{6}$ of the book on Monday. She read $\frac{2}{3}$ of the book on Tuesday. What fraction of the book has Gia read in all?

SOLUTION

1 Sketch a rectangle to show $\frac{1}{6}$.

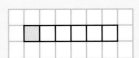

Below that rectangle, sketch another rectangle the same size that shows $\frac{2}{3}$.

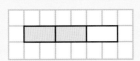

2 Add parts of the whole that are the same size. To add thirds and sixths, find a fraction equivalent to $\frac{2}{3}$ that has a denominator of 6.

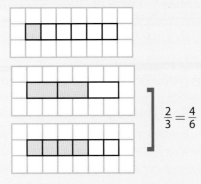

$$\frac{2}{3} = \frac{4}{6}$$

3 Count sixths on both rectangles.

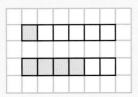

There are 5 sixths in all, or $\frac{5}{6}$.

4 Sketch the answer $\frac{5}{6}$ on a new rectangle and draw a blank rectangle below it the same size. Since you cannot sketch a fraction equivalent to $\frac{5}{6}$ using a larger fraction, $\frac{5}{6}$ is in simplest form.

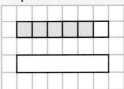

5 Show your work and write the solution.

$$\frac{1}{6} = \frac{1}{6}$$
$$+\frac{2}{3} = +\frac{4}{6}$$
$$\overline{\phantom{+\frac{2}{3}=+}\frac{5}{6}}$$

ANSWER Gia read $\frac{5}{6}$ of her book.

LEARN

Solve. Sketch a picture to add or subtract. Write the answer in simplest form.

1. Heather has a ribbon that is $\frac{4}{6}$ foot long. She gives $\frac{1}{3}$ foot of the ribbon to her friend.

   How much ribbon does Heather have left?

2. In an art studio, $\frac{1}{2}$ of the construction paper is red and $\frac{1}{4}$ of the construction paper is blue. The rest of the paper is white.

   What fraction of the pack of paper is red or blue?

3. A pitcher has $\frac{2}{6}$ gallon of orange juice and $\frac{2}{6}$ gallon of pineapple juice.

   How much juice is in the pitcher in all?

4. June has $\frac{5}{6}$ cup of yogurt. She eats $\frac{1}{3}$ cup of the yogurt.

   How much of the yogurt is left?

Add and Subtract Fractions (B)

Add or Subtract Like Denominators

Worked Examples

You can use number lines to add or subtract fractions with like denominators.

PROBLEM 1 Ron bought $\frac{5}{6}$ of a yard of canvas for a camp project. He did not have enough canvas, so he bought another $\frac{2}{6}$ of a yard of canvas. How much canvas did Ron buy?

SOLUTION

1 Number Line 1: Sketch $\frac{5}{6}$.

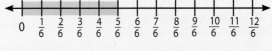

2 Number Line 2: Sketch $\frac{2}{6}$.

3 Number Line 3: Begin at $\frac{5}{6}$ and sketch $\frac{2}{6}$ to add $\frac{5}{6} + \frac{2}{6}$.

4 Number Line 4: Simplify the answer, if necessary. Because $\frac{7}{6}$ is an improper fraction, change it to a mixed number to simplify it. Look at Number Line 4 to find the mixed number.

ANSWER Ron bought $1\frac{1}{6}$ yards of canvas.

$$\begin{array}{r} \frac{5}{6} \\ + \ \frac{2}{6} \\ \hline \frac{7}{6} = 1\frac{1}{6} \end{array}$$

LEARN

PROBLEM 2 There are $1\frac{2}{3}$ boxes of graham crackers. To make campfire snacks, the campers use $1\frac{1}{3}$ boxes. What fraction of a box of graham crackers is left?

SOLUTION

1 Number Line 1: Sketch $1\frac{2}{3}$.

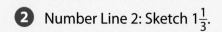

2 Number Line 2: Sketch $1\frac{1}{3}$.

3 Number Line 3: To subtract $1\frac{1}{3}$ from $1\frac{2}{3}$, change $1\frac{1}{3}$ to an improper fraction. Look at Number Line 3 to find the improper fraction equivalent to $1\frac{1}{3}$.

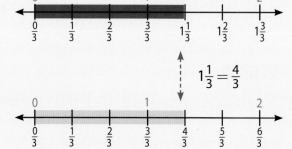

$$1\frac{1}{3} = \frac{4}{3}$$

4 Number Line 1: Jump back $\frac{4}{3}$ to subtract $1\frac{1}{3}$ from $1\frac{2}{3}$.

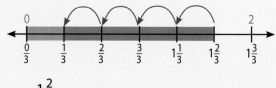

$1\frac{2}{3} - 1\frac{1}{3} = \frac{1}{3}$, and $\frac{1}{3}$ is in simplest form.

$$\begin{array}{r} 1\frac{2}{3} \\ -\ 1\frac{1}{3} \\ \hline \frac{1}{3} \end{array}$$

ANSWER There is $\frac{1}{3}$ of a box of graham crackers left.

LEARN

Solve. Use number lines to add or subtract. Write the answer in simplest form.

1. Serena swam $1\frac{1}{2}$ miles on Saturday and $1\frac{1}{2}$ miles on Sunday.

   How far did Serena swim altogether?

2. Alexander had $\frac{3}{4}$ cup of raisins. He and his friends ate $\frac{2}{4}$ cup.

   How much of the raisins were left?

3. The cookie recipe uses $1\frac{1}{3}$ cups of white sugar and $\frac{1}{3}$ cup of brown sugar.

   How much sugar is in the cookie recipe altogether?

Add and Subtract Fractions (B)

Add or Subtract Unlike Denominators

Worked Examples

You can use number lines to help you add or subtract fractions with unlike denominators.

PROBLEM 1 In Maria's choir, $\frac{1}{2}$ of the members have red folders and $\frac{2}{6}$ of the members have white folders. The rest of the members have blue folders. What fraction of the choir members have red folders or white folders?

SOLUTION

1 Sketch $\frac{1}{2}$ on the first number line.

2 Sketch $\frac{2}{6}$ on the second number line.

3 Mark the first number line to show sixths.

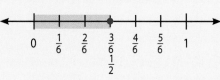

4 Begin at $\frac{3}{6}$ and sketch $\frac{2}{6}$ more on the first number line.

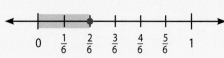

ANSWER $\frac{5}{6}$ of the choir members have red or white folders.

$$
\begin{array}{rcl}
\frac{1}{2} & = & \frac{3}{6} \\
+\ \frac{2}{6} & = & +\frac{2}{6} \\
\hline
& = & \frac{5}{6}
\end{array}
$$

PROBLEM 2 The yellow hiking trail is $1\frac{5}{6}$ miles long. The red hiking trail is $1\frac{2}{3}$ miles long. How much longer is the yellow hiking trail than the red hiking trail?

SOLUTION

1 Sketch $1\frac{5}{6}$ on the first number line.

2 Sketch $1\frac{2}{3}$ on the second number line.

3 Mark the second number line to show sixths.

4 Compare the number lines to subtract. The $1\frac{5}{6}$ bar is $\frac{1}{6}$ longer than the $1\frac{4}{6}$ bar, so $1\frac{5}{6} - 1\frac{4}{6} = \frac{1}{6}$. Since $1\frac{4}{6} = 1\frac{2}{3}$, $1\frac{5}{6} - 1\frac{2}{3} = \frac{1}{6}$.

ANSWER The yellow hiking trail is $\frac{1}{6}$ mile longer than the red hiking trail.

$$
\begin{array}{r}
1\frac{5}{6} = 1\frac{5}{6} \\
- 1\frac{2}{3} = - 1\frac{4}{6} \\
\hline
= \frac{1}{6}
\end{array}
$$

Solve. Use number lines to add or subtract. Write the answer in simplest form.

1. Winnie had $1\frac{2}{3}$ yards of wire. She bought $1\frac{1}{6}$ yards more.

   How much wire does Winnie have in all?

L E A R N

2. Johnny has $\frac{3}{4}$ cup of sugar. He uses $\frac{1}{2}$ cup to make a smoothie.

    How much sugar is left?

3. Vanessa ate $\frac{2}{6}$ of a granola bar for breakfast and $\frac{1}{2}$ of the granola bar for a snack.

    How much of the granola bar did Vanessa eat altogether?

4. Farmer Brown planted $1\frac{1}{4}$ pounds of seed in the morning. He planted $1\frac{1}{2}$ pounds of seed in the afternoon.

    How many pounds of seed did Farmer Brown plant altogether?

Unlike Denominators (A)

Use Common Denominators

Use the least common denominator to rewrite the expression.

1. $\frac{3}{4} - \frac{1}{3}$

2. $\frac{5}{8} + \frac{1}{4}$

Solve.

3. $\frac{5}{6} - \frac{1}{4} = \frac{?}{\rule{1cm}{0.4pt}}$

4. $\frac{2}{5} + \frac{1}{2} = \frac{?}{\rule{1cm}{0.4pt}}$

5. $\frac{1}{4} + \frac{1}{3} = \frac{?}{\rule{1cm}{0.4pt}}$

6. $\frac{1}{2} + \frac{1}{4} = \frac{?}{\rule{1cm}{0.4pt}}$

7. Debbie walked her dog along a rectangular path, which had a length of $\frac{5}{6}$ mile and a width of $\frac{1}{3}$ mile. The dog walked one length of the rectangle and one width of the rectangle, and then stopped to drink water. How far did Debbie's dog walk before stopping for water?

Choose the answer.

8. $\frac{1}{3} + \frac{3}{6} = ?$

    A. $\frac{4}{3}$ B. $\frac{4}{6}$

    C. $\frac{5}{6}$ D. $\frac{4}{9}$

9. $\frac{3}{4} - \frac{1}{2} = ?$

    A. $\frac{2}{2}$ B. $\frac{2}{3}$

    C. $\frac{1}{2}$ D. $\frac{1}{4}$

10. Aisha bought $\frac{1}{2}$ lb of sliced turkey and $\frac{1}{4}$ lb of sliced ham. How much meat did Aisha buy?

    A. $\frac{2}{2}$ lb   B. $\frac{3}{4}$ lb   C. $\frac{1}{6}$ lb   D. $\frac{2}{6}$ lb

11. Bobby skated $\frac{4}{6}$ of a mile on Monday and $\frac{2}{3}$ of a mile on Tuesday. How far did Bobby skate? Be sure the answer is in simplest form.

    A. $2\frac{1}{3}$ miles   B. $\frac{3}{6}$ mile   C. $1\frac{1}{3}$ miles   D. $1\frac{3}{6}$ miles

12. Gina had $1\frac{1}{3}$ pints of lemonade. She drank some and had $\frac{1}{6}$ pint left over. How much lemonade did Gina drink?

    A. $1\frac{1}{6}$ pints   B. 2 pints   C. $1\frac{1}{3}$ pints   D. $\frac{1}{2}$ pint

T R Y   I T

Different Ways to Write Products

Different Products

Answer the question.

1. Sara knew that $18 \times 2 = 36$. What is another way to write 36 as a product of factors?

2. How can you write 50 as a product of only prime numbers?

3. Write three number sentences in which each product is equal to 40.

Choose the answer.

4. Jerome had 12 squares. He made this rectangle.

Which other rectangle could he make with 12 squares?

A.

B.

C.

D.

5. Jackson had 12 squares. He made this rectangle.

Which other rectangle could he make with 12 squares?

A. 2 unit $\times$ 12 unit rectangle

B. 2 unit $\times$ 6 unit rectangle

C. 3 unit $\times$ 6 unit rectangle

D. 8 unit $\times$ 2 unit rectangle

6. Regan knew that $60 = 10 \times 6$. Which expression also equals 60?

A. 4×20 B. 5×12

C. 8×8 D. 9×6

7. Tom wrote $10 \times 10 = 100$. Which equation is also correct?

A. $2 \times 40 = 100$ B. $4 \times 15 = 100$

C. $5 \times 20 = 100$ D. $8 \times 12 = 100$

8. Which equations equal 12? Choose **two**.

A. $1 \times 11 = 12$ B. $2 \times 6 = 12$

C. $4 \times 4 = 12$ D. $3 \times 4 = 12$

9. Which equations equal 24? Choose **two**.

A. $1 \times 24 = 24$ B. $2 \times 8 = 24$

C. $4 \times 4 = 24$ D. $2 \times 12 = 24$

10. Which is another way to write $5 \times 12 = 60$?

A. $60 = 2 \times 2 \times 3 \times 5$

B. $60 = 2 \times 5 \times 5$

C. $60 = 2 \times 2 \times 12$

D. $60 = 5 \times 10 + 2$

TRY IT

Fraction Factors (B)

Multiply Fractions by Whole Numbers

Worked Examples

You can use grid paper to model multiplying a fraction by a whole number. When a numerator and a denominator have a common factor, you can simplify before you multiply.

PROBLEM $\frac{1}{4} \times 12 = ?$

SOLUTION

1 On grid paper, draw a rectangle around 12 small grid squares.

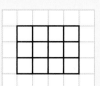

2 The rectangle is divided into 4 equal-sized columns, or fourths. Shade one column, or $\frac{1}{4}$ of 12 squares.

3 Count the small grid squares that are shaded. 3 squares out of 12 are shaded, so $\frac{1}{4} \times 12 = 3$.

ANSWER 3

Simplify, if possible. Then solve.

1. $\frac{1}{8} \times 16 = \underline{\ ?\ }$

2. $\frac{2}{4} \times 20 = \underline{\ ?\ }$

L E A R N

3. $\frac{1}{5} \times 15 = \underline{\ ?\ }$

4. $\frac{2}{10} \times 25 = ?$

$\frac{?}{5} \times 25 = \underline{\ ?\ }$

5. $\frac{1}{4} \times 24 = \underline{\ ?\ }$

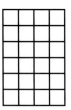

6. $\frac{6}{8} \times 32 = ?$

$\frac{?}{?} \times 32 = \underline{\ ?\ }$

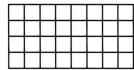

Solve. You may sketch the problem on grid paper if necessary.

7. $\frac{1}{5} \times 20 = \underline{\ ?\ }$

$\frac{2}{5} \times 20 = \underline{\ ?\ }$

$\frac{3}{5} \times 20 = \underline{\ ?\ }$

$\frac{4}{5} \times 20 = \underline{\ ?\ }$

$\frac{5}{5} \times 20 = \underline{\ ?\ }$

8. $\frac{1}{4} \times 36 = \underline{\ ?\ }$

$\frac{2}{4} \times 36 = \underline{\ ?\ }$

$\frac{3}{4} \times 36 = \underline{\ ?\ }$

$\frac{4}{4} \times 36 = \underline{\ ?\ }$

9. Julie knows that

$\frac{1}{4} \times 20 = 5.$

How can she use this to find $\frac{3}{4} \times 20$?

Fraction Factors (B)

Products of Fractions and Whole Numbers

Worked Examples

You can simplify factors before you multiply a fraction by a whole number to solve a story problem.

PROBLEM 1 Rosa recorded 48 minutes of music. She listens to $\frac{3}{4}$ of the music. How many minutes of music does Rosa listen to?

SOLUTION Multiply to solve the problem. Use the method that is easiest for you. One way is shown below.

1 $\frac{3}{4}$ of 48 means $\frac{3}{4} \times 48$.

2 $\frac{3}{4} \times 48 = \frac{3}{4} \times \frac{48}{1}$ ← The fraction $\frac{3}{4}$ is in simplest form, so you don't need to simplify.

3 $= \frac{3 \times 48}{4 \times 1}$

4 $= \frac{144}{4} = 144 \div 4 = 36$

ANSWER Rosa listens to 36 minutes of music.

PROBLEM 2 Marcus collected 90 state quarters. Exactly $\frac{8}{12}$ of them are California quarters. How many California quarters does Marcus have?

SOLUTION Simpify before you multiply.

$$90 \times \frac{8}{12} = ?$$

$$90 \times \frac{8 \div 4}{12 \div 4} = ?$$

$$90 \times \frac{2}{3} = \frac{90}{1} \times \frac{2}{3}$$

$$= \frac{90 \times 2}{1 \times 3}$$

$$= \frac{180}{3} = 180 \div 3 = 60$$

ANSWER Marcus has 60 California quarters.

L E A R N

Simplify the fraction or fraction factors, if possible. Then solve.

1. Jenna has an animal pen with 96 feet of fence around it. A swinging gate is $\frac{1}{8}$ as long as the total fence.

   How many feet long is the gate?

2. Danny is $\frac{8}{10}$ as tall as his older sister. His sister is 60 inches tall.

   How tall is Danny?

3. There are 56 ounces of soup left in the chowder pot. The pot will be empty if each person has $\frac{2}{16}$ of the soup.

   How much soup will each person get?

4. Rosa practices piano for 63 minutes. She spends $\frac{1}{3}$ of the time practicing scales.

   How many minutes does Rosa practice scales?

5. Jeffrey read $\frac{4}{12}$ of his book.

   If his book has 90 pages, how many pages did Jeffrey read?

Challenge Question

Write and solve fraction problems to answer the questions.

6. Doug spends $\frac{7}{8}$ of his $64, and Kendra spends $\frac{10}{12}$ of her $78.
   Who has more money left? How much more?

LEARN

Fraction and Whole Number Products (A)

Multiply and Simplify

Worked Examples

You can multiply a fraction by a whole number by using a model and by using an algorithm, or a step-by-step process.

PROBLEM   Naomi has 9 eggs. She makes an omelet with $\frac{1}{3}$ of the eggs. How many eggs does she use?

SOLUTION 1   The model shows that every 3 thirds equals 1. So 6 thirds equals 2 and 9 thirds equals 3.

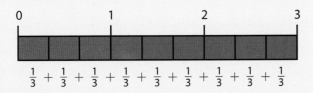

$$\frac{1}{3} + \frac{1}{3} + \frac{1}{3} + \frac{1}{3} + \frac{1}{3} + \frac{1}{3} + \frac{1}{3} + \frac{1}{3} + \frac{1}{3}$$

SOLUTION 2 $\frac{1}{3} \times 9 = \frac{1}{3} \times \frac{9}{1}$

$$= \frac{1 \times 9}{3 \times 1}$$

$$= \frac{9}{3} = 9 \div 3 = 3$$

ANSWER   Naomi uses 3 eggs to make her omelet.

Solve.

1. The coaches reported that 20 children were at soccer practice last Saturday. If $\frac{1}{5}$ of the children wore green jerseys, how many children wore green jerseys?

2. Chuck has $72. He buys a book with $\frac{1}{8}$ of his money. How much does he spend on the book?

L E A R N

3. Robinson's basketball team scored 50 points in the first half of a game. Robinson scored $\frac{1}{2}$ of those points. How many points did he score?

4. The food pantry has 60 pounds of flour. Volunteers give out $\frac{5}{6}$ of the flour in one morning. How many pounds of flour do they give out?

5. George's grandma is $\frac{7}{10}$ the age of his great-grandma. His great-grandma is 90 years old. How old is George's grandma?

6. Melanie has 12 cups of soup stock. She wants to use $\frac{1}{4}$ of it in a recipe. How many cups will she use?

7. There are 88 miles of shelves in the library's basement. If $\frac{1}{8}$ of the shelves hold soft-cover books, how many miles of shelves of soft-cover books are in the basement?

LEARN

Compare Decimals

Greater or Less?

Worked Examples

You can use a greater-than symbol (>) to order and compare numbers from greatest to least. You can use a less-than symbol (<) to order and compare numbers from least to greatest.

PROBLEM Use > and < to write two statements to compare 320.3 and 320.03.

SOLUTION

1 320.30 and 320.03 — Write numbers with the same number of decimal places, if needed.

2 3 tenths > 0 tenths — Start at the far left place-value position. Find the first pair of digits that differ. Compare them.

3 320.3 > 320.03 — Write a comparison statement using the numbers 320.3 and 320.03 from the original problem.

4 320.03 < 320.3 — Reverse the order of the numbers 320.3 and 320.03 from the original problem and use the correct symbol to compare them.

ANSWER 320.3 > 320.03, 320.03 < 320.3

Use > and < to write **two** statements to compare the numbers.

1. 1,323.99 and 1,324.01
2. 203.02 and 20.32
3. 78.45 and 78.48

Use <, >, or = to compare the numbers.

4. 106.06 __?__ 106.60
5. 34.3 __?__ 34.30
6. 3,482.3 __?__ 3,482.08

L E A R N

Solve.

7. Monya has two large dogs. Sandy weighs 50.2 kg
and Mocca weighs 50.19 kg.
Which dog weighs less, or do they weigh the same?

8. Caryn threw a ball 34.62 m. George threw a ball 34.7 m.
Who threw the ball farther, or did they throw the
same distance?

9. Molly swam 32.9 laps. Tom swam 32.90 laps.
Who swam farther, or did they swim the same distance?

Order Three Decimal Numbers

Order Numbers

Worked Examples

You can order decimal numbers in the same way that you order whole numbers. You start at the left-most digit and compare the values of the digits in the same place-value position. You find the greatest number, the least number, and the number in-between these numbers. Then you order the numbers and insert greater-than symbols ($>$) or less-than symbols ($<$) as directed.

PROBLEM A bag of raisins weighs 5.34 oz. A bag of dried peaches weighs 5.7 oz. A bag of dried apricots weighs 4.98 oz. What comparison statement shows the weight of the fruit ordered from least to greatest?

SOLUTION

1 Refer to this place-value chart, if you wish.

Millions		Hundred Thousands	Ten Thousands	Thousands		Hundreds	Tens	Ones		Tenths	Hundredths	Thousandths
	,				,				.			

2 Make a chart to organize your numbers.

Greatest	
In-Between	
Least	

3 To compare 5.34, 5.7, 4.98, start at the left-most digit and compare the values of the digits in the same place-value position. First find the greatest and least numbers.

In the ones place, 4 is less than the two 5s, so 4.98 is the least number. Write it in the chart and cross it off the list.

In the tenths place, 7 is greater than 3, so 5.7 is the greatest number. Write it in the chart and cross it off the list. (Write 5.7 as 5.70, if you wish.)

Greatest	5.7
In-Between	
Least	4.98

5.34
~~5.7~~
~~4.98~~

The number that remains, 5.34, is in-between the greatest and least numbers. Write it in the chart and cross it off the list.

Greatest	5.7
In-Between	5.34
Least	4.98

~~5.34~~
~~5.7~~
~~4.98~~

4 Read the problem again and order from least to greatest: 4.98, 5.34, 5.7.

5 Use the less-than symbol (<) to write a comparison statement: 4.98 < 5.34 < 5.7.

ANSWER 4.98 < 5.34 < 5.7

Read the problem and follow the directions.

1. Write 513.45, 514.5, and 154.1 in order from greatest to least.

2. Write 627.45, 672.45, and 627.5 in order from least to greatest.

3. A bag of raisins weighs 5.34 oz. A bag of dried peaches weighs 5.7 oz. A bag of dried apricots weighs 4.98 oz. Order the names of the fruit from the greatest weight to the least weight.

Solve.

4. Maya incorrectly wrote a comparison statement to order
   3.4, 3.04, and 3.14 from greatest to least this way:
   3.4 > 3.04 > 3.14.

   Why is her answer incorrect?

5. Jeff incorrectly wrote a comparison statement to order 25.4, 23.9,
   and 25.29 from least to greatest this way:
   25.4 > 25.29 > 23.9.

   Why is his answer incorrect?

6. A bag of raisins weighs 5.34 oz. A bag of dried peaches weighs 5.7 oz.
   A bag of dried apricots weighs 4.98 oz.

   What comparison statement shows the weight of the fruit ordered
   from least to greatest?

Use the table to solve.

7. In a swim race, the fastest time, or
   least number of seconds, wins the
   race. Write the names of the children
   in order from fastest to slowest times
   for the race.

50-Meter Race Results	
Name	**Seconds**
Kate	57.8
Jake	59.01
Ivy	58.8
Dean	57.35
Aiden	57.83

LEARN

Order Three Decimal Numbers

Write Comparison Statements

Complete the comparison statement.

1. 37.12, 37.2, 37.02

   _?_ < _?_ < _?_

2. 100.09, 99.10, 100.9

   _?_ > _?_ > _?_

Read the problem and follow the directions.

3. Bea rode her bike 18.49 miles. Tina rode her bike 18.04 miles. Rob rode his bike 18.45 miles. Use two > symbols to order the miles from greatest to least. 18.49 18.45 18.04

4. Bea rode her bike 18.49 miles. Tina rode her bike 18.04 miles. Rob rode his bike 18.45 miles. Use two < symbols to order the miles from least to greatest. 18.04 18.45 18.49

5. Write the decimals 45.78, 45.7, and 45.87 in order from least to greatest. 45.7 45.78 45.87

6. Write the decimals 33.06, 33.64, and 33.60 in order from greatest to least. 33.64 33.60 33.06

7. Cheryl threw the ball 15.6 m. Gina threw the ball 15.72 m. Joanne threw the ball 15.67 m. Marta threw the ball 15.06 m. Write the names of the girls in order from the longest throw to the shortest throw. gina Joanne

8. Susana used 6.75 cubic feet of soil. Rob used 6.07 cubic feet of soil. Lucy used 6.55 cubic feet of soil. Matt used 6.25 cubic feet of soil. Write the names of the children in order from the least soil used to the most soil used.

9. Bea rode her bike 18.49 miles. Tina rode her bike 18.04 miles. Rob rode his bike 18.45 miles. Order the names from the longest to the shortest distance they rode.

Choose the answer.

10. Which shows the decimals 56.7, 56.73, and 56.37 written in order from greatest to least?

    A. 56.73, 56.7, 56.37

    B. 56.7, 56.37, 56.73

    C. 56.73, 56.37, 56.7

    D. 56.7, 56.73, 56.37

11. Corrine compared the decimals 11.46, 11.98, and 11.34. Which is correct?

    A. $11.46 > 11.98 > 11.34$

    B. $11.34 > 11.46 > 11.98$

    C. $11.98 > 11.34 > 11.46$

    D. $11.98 > 11.46 > 11.34$

12. Peter compared the decimals 794.77, 794.99, and 794.33. Which is correct?

    A. $794.77 < 794.99 < 794.33$

    B. $794.33 < 794.77 < 794.99$

    C. $794.99 < 794.77 < 794.33$

    D. $794.33 < 794.99 < 794.77$

13. Megan compared the decimals 66.64, 66.46, and 64.66. Which is correct?

    A. $66.64 < 64.66 < 66.46$

    B. $64.66 < 66.46 < 66.64$

    C. $66.46 < 66.64 < 64.66$

    D. $66.64 < 66.46 < 64.66$

14. Jeff weighs 77.4 pounds. Gordon weighs 77.82 pounds. Lucas weighs 77.28 pounds. Xander weighs 77.04 pounds. Which shows these boys ordered from the least weight to the greatest weight?

    A. Jeff, Gordon, Lucas, Xander

    B. Gordon, Xander, Lucas, Jeff

    C. Lucas, Jeff, Xander, Gordon

    D. Xander, Lucas, Jeff, Gordon

15. Joseph bought a packet of tortillas that weighed 1.35 kg. Martin bought a packet of tortillas that weighed 1.55 kg. Phil bought a packet of tortillas that weighed 1.85 kg. Arnold bought a packet of tortillas that weighed 1.65 kg. Write the names of the boys in order from the heaviest packet of tortillas bought to the lightest packet of tortillas bought.

    A. Phil, Arnold, Martin, Joseph

    B. Arnold, Martin, Phil, Joseph

    C. Martin, Phil, Arnold, Joseph

    D. Joseph, Martin, Phil, Arnold

Challenge Question

Solve.

16. Three food choices cost $2.89, $2.09, and $2.98. Hot dogs cost less than hamburgers. Hamburgers cost more than veggie burgers. Veggie burgers cost more than hot dogs. Use $<$ or $>$ to order the prices from greatest to least. Then write the names of the foods in order from least to most expensive.

T R Y   I T

Decimal Numbers and Rounding

Pick the Correct Rounded Number

Worked Examples

Rounding is appropriate when you don't need an exact answer. You can round a decimal number by using a number line or by using place value.

PROBLEM Answer the question. Then state whether rounding is appropriate in this situation. Explain why or why not.

- The tiger eats 104.2 lb of food a day. Rick said the tiger eats about 104 lb of food each day. Lenore said the tiger eats about 105 lb of food each day. Paula said the tiger eats about 110 lb of food each day. Anne said the tiger eats about 94 lb of food each day. Which person correctly rounded the amount that a tiger eats each day to the nearest pound?

SOLUTION 1 Use a number line.

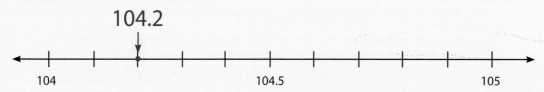

104.2

104   104.5   105

On the number line, 104.2 is closer to the whole number 104 than to the whole number 105. Since 104 is the rounded number, Rick rounded correctly.

SOLUTION 2

1 Use a place-value chart, or write the place-value names above each digit of the number.

Hundred Thousands	Ten Thousands	Thousands		Hundreds	Tens	Ones		Tenths	Hundredths	Thousandths
			,	1	0	4̲	.	②		

2 Underline the place-value position you must round to, or the *rounding place*. You are asked to round to the nearest pound, which is the nearest whole number, or the ones place. So underline the 4 in the ones place.

3 Circle the digit in the position to the right of the rounding place. Circle the digit in the tenths place, or 2.

104.2

4 If the circled digit is greater than or equal to 5, the digit in the rounding place increases by 1. Since the circled digit 2 is not greater than or equal to 5, move to the next step.

hundreds
tens
ones
tenths
10**4**.②

5 If the circled digit is less than 5, the digit in the rounding place stays the same. Since the circled digit 2 is less than 5, the digit in the rounding place stays 4 and everything to the right of the ones place is dropped. So the digit 2 is dropped and 104 is the rounded answer. Rick rounded correctly.

ANSWER Rick rounded correctly. Rounding is appropriate in this situation. The amount of food that a tiger eats per day will never be exact. So rounding to the nearest pound, or nearest whole number, is appropriate and convenient.

Solve.

1. The cheetah at the zoo weighs 95.63 lb. Lee said the cheetah weighs about 95 lb. Tony said the cheetah weighs about 100 lb. Jordan said the cheetah weighs about 96 lb. Brian said the cheetah weighs about 90 lb. Which person correctly rounded the weight of the cheetah to the nearest pound?

2. Randy and his family are planning a trip to the zoo. Randy finds directions online. The directions say that the distance from Randy's house to the zoo is 52.75 miles. Randy rounds the distance to the nearest tenth of a mile. Which is the distance correctly rounded to the nearest tenth: 53.0 miles, 52.7 miles, 52.8 miles, or 50.0 miles?

3. Mr. Ortiz must replace a broken bar on the monkey cage. The bar is 35.45 inches long. Which is the length of the bar rounded to the nearest whole inch: 35 inches, 36 inches, 40 inches, or 35.5 inches?

4. The zoo's annual fun run is this weekend. Runners will run on a path through and around the zoo. They will run a total distance of 5.86 miles. Carrie says the run is about 6.0 miles long. Gina says the run is about 5.8 miles long. Eric says the run is about 5.9 miles long. Which person correctly rounded the distance to the nearest tenth of a mile?

5. Carrie, Gina, and Eric ran in the zoo's annual fun run. Gina finished the race in 65.37 minutes. She finished just seconds before Eric, and about a minute after Carrie. Which of the following shows Gina's time rounded to the nearest minute: 65 minutes, 66 minutes, 60 minutes, or 70 minutes?

L E A R N

Decimal Numbers and Rounding

Practice Rounding Decimal Numbers

Round the number to the nearest whole number.

1. 28.37

2. 99.572

Round the number to the nearest tenth.

3. 270.84

4. 53.64

Use the statements below to answer Problems 5 and 6.

> Rusty is following instructions to build a birdhouse. The instructions say to cut a piece of wood 20.32 cm long and 16.51 cm wide.

5. If Rusty had rounded each measurement to the nearest centimeter, what would his rounded dimensions have been?

6. Is rounding appropriate for this situation? Why or why not?

Solve.

7. Doreen spent $25.55 on groceries. Round this number to the nearest dollar.

$26.55

8. Zoe is 5.54 ft tall. Round this number to the nearest tenth of a foot.

Choose the answer.

9. The price of a movie ticket was $12.75. Ben said the price was about $13. Charlie said the price was about $12. Susan said the price was about $15. Rebecca said the price was about $10. Who correctly rounded the price of the movie ticket to the nearest dollar?

   A. Ben   B. Charlie   C. Susan   D. Rebecca

10. A box of baseball bats weighs 6.25 lb. Trent said the box weighs about 6.0 lb. Emmitt said the box weighs about 10.0 lb. Barry said the box weighs about 6.2 lb. Walter said the box weighs about 6.3 lb. Who correctly rounded the weight of the box to the nearest tenth of a pound?

   A. Trent   B. Emmitt   C. Barry   D. Walter

TRY IT

11. The band marched for 3.65 km. Maria said the band marched about 3.0 km. Sandee said the band marched about 3.5 km. Mark said the band marched about 3.6 km. Bernard said the band marched about 3.7 km. Who correctly rounded the distance the band marched to the nearest tenth of a kilometer?

A. Maria   B. Sandee   C. Mark   D. Bernard

12. Look at the problems below. There is only one situation where it would be acceptable to round the numbers. Which one is it?

A. The pattern calls for a piece of lace 2.1 yd long and another piece 3.6 yd long. The seamstress is thinking about rounding each to the nearest whole number and cutting pieces 2 yd and 4 yd long.

B. Beverly is buying lunch at a restaurant. She wants to buy a sandwich that costs $5.25 and a glass of milk that costs $2.15. She has $7.00. She is thinking of rounding to the nearest whole number and adding $5 and $2.

C. Derek needs 1.4 m of wood to finish his fence and 1.25 m of wood to finish his shed. He is thinking of rounding to the nearest whole number and buying 2 m of wood.

D. A rosebush costs $12.95 and a shrub costs $18.75. Desiree wants to buy both plants but must make sure she has enough money. She is thinking about rounding each number to the nearest dollar and adding $13.00 and $19.00.

13. Look at the problems below. There is only one situation where it would be acceptable to round the numbers. Which one is it?

A. Diana is buying a gift for $26.75 and a card for $2.75 and wants to make sure she has enough money. She is thinking about rounding to the nearest whole dollar and bringing $30 to the store.

B. Trish is ordering her meal and wants to make sure she has enough money. She has $15.00. She wants a salad for $4.95, the pasta special for $9.25, and a glass of milk for $1.25. She is thinking about rounding each amount to the nearest dollar.

C. Mia is baking and needs 1.25 cups of walnuts for muffins and 2.25 cups for the loaves of banana bread. She is thinking about rounding each amount to the nearest whole number and buying 3 cups of walnuts.

D. Richard is buying trim for his office and needs pieces of 7.35 m and 4.75 m long. He is thinking about rounding to the nearest whole number and buying 12 m trim.

TRY IT

14. Look at the problems below. There is only one situation where it would be acceptable to round the numbers. Which one is it?

A. The cook at the summer camp needs 4.75 quarts of apple juice and 7.45 quarts of orange juice. The cook is thinking about rounding to the nearest whole number and buying 12 quarts of juice.

B. A carpenter needs 6.4 m plain molding and 8.3 m fancy molding. The carpenter is thinking of rounding each amount to the nearest whole number and buying 14 m molding.

C. The video game costs $18.75. The cashier is thinking about rounding the price to the nearest whole dollar and giving the customer $1.00 change.

D. Marilyn wants to buy a pair of pants and a T-shirt. The pants she wants cost $25.75 and the T-shirt costs $13.95. She brought $40 to the store and wants to make sure she has enough money. She plans to round each price to the nearest whole dollar.

Add and Subtract Decimal Numbers

Use a Data Table to Estimate

Worked Examples

Estimating can help you decide if a sum or difference is reasonable. You estimate the sum or difference first, compute next, and then compare the two results.

PROBLEM   Use the data table to answer the questions.

- Estimate how much a dime and a quarter weigh together. Round each weight to the nearest gram and use the rounded numbers to compute. Then find the exact weight of the two coins.

Facts About U.S Coins						
Coin	Penny	Nickel	Dime	Quarter	Half-dollar	Dollar
Weight	2.50 g	5.00 g	2.27 g	5.67 g	11.34 g	8.1 g
Diameter	19.05 mm	21.21 mm	17.91 mm	24.26 mm	30.61 mm	26.5 mm
Thickness	1.55 mm	1.95 mm	1.35 mm	1.75 mm	2.15 mm	2 mm

SOLUTION

1 On the data table, find the weight of a dime and of a quarter. ⟶ Dime, 2.27 g
Quarter, 5.67g

2 Decide what operation you use to find the weights of the two coins together. ⟶ Addition

3 To the nearest gram, or whole number, round 2.27 g to 2 g and 5.67 g to 6 g. Add 2 g and 6 g to estimate the sum. ⟶ Estimate: about 8 g

4 Now find the exact sum. Use grid paper to align decimal points and digits in the same place-value positions.

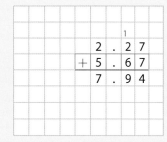

ANSWER   Estimate: about 8 g; Exact: 7.94 g

L E A R N

Round each measurement to the nearest whole number. Use the rounded numbers to estimate the answer. Then find the exact answer to the problem.

1. How much heavier is a half-dollar coin than a dollar coin?

2. How much wider is a quarter than a penny?

3. Which is wider, a dollar coin or a quarter? How much wider?

4. Nella stacks a penny and a nickel. How many millimeters high is her stack of coins?

5. Mark has some coins that weigh 7.27 grams altogether. He adds a half-dollar to his coins. Now how much do his coins weigh?

6. If you stack a dime, a quarter, and a dollar coin, will the stack be more or less than 6 mm high? How do you know without actually adding the thickness of the coins?

Challenge Question

Use the data table. Round each measurement to the nearest whole number and estimate the sum or difference. Then answer the question and use the estimate to check that your answer is reasonable.

7. How much will your coins weigh if you have one of each coin in the chart?

Add and Subtract Decimal Numbers

Estimate and Solve

Round to the nearest tenth. Then estimate by adding or subtracting the rounded numbers.

1. $3.58 + 4 + 6.22 = \underline{\ ?\ }$

2. $47.07 - 9.53 = \underline{\ ?\ }$

3. $123.6 - 47.79 = \underline{\ ?\ }$

4. $109.73 + 5{,}126.19 = \underline{\ ?\ }$

Solve.

5. A champion fir tree in Redwood National Park is 257.00 ft tall. How much taller is the champion tree than a fir tree that is 41.72 ft tall?

6. According to the U.S. Mint, a dime weighs 2.27 g, a half-dollar coin weighs 11.34 g, and a dollar coin weighs 8.1 g. What is the total weight of the three coins?

7. $652.68 + 32.4 = \underline{\ ?\ }$

8. $934.61 - 45.82 = \underline{\ ?\ }$

9. $129.6 - 43.13 = \underline{\ ?\ }$

10. Tamika, her mother, and her grandmother are going to the zoo to celebrate Tamika's eighth birthday. How much will it cost for admission for the three people?

ZOO ADMISSION PRICES
Adult.......................$12.98
Child..........................$7.25

TRY IT

11. Jason bought some supplies at the store. How much will it cost for 1 notebook, 1 pencil box, and 1 pen?

PRICES

Notebook.......$3.50

Pencil Box $7.45

Pen $1.29

Choose the answer.

12. Geoff bought a T-shirt that cost $9.98 and a pair of jeans that cost $34.98. About how much did Geoff spend?

A. $20   B. $25   C. $45   D. $50

13. Anita is on a hiking trail that is 5.9 km long. She has walked 4.2 km. About how much farther does Anita have to walk?

A. 0.1 km   B. 1 km   C. 2 km   D. 10 km

14. Ms. Hanover is fixing some wires. She needs pieces of wire that are 4.8 ft, 3.9 ft, and 12.5 ft long. She wants to make sure she buys enough wire but not too much extra. How much wire should she buy?

A. 5 ft   B. 13 ft   C. 22 ft   D. 30 ft

TRY IT

Equivalent Decimals and Fractions

Decimals and Fractions

Worked Examples

You can write equivalent decimal numbers for fractions expressed in tenths and hundredths. You can also write equivalent fractions for decimal numbers expressed in tenths and hundredths.

PROBLEM Use a decimal place-value chart or a number line to solve the problem.

- Rosa listened to 0.3 of a song. Write one equivalent decimal number and two equivalent fractions that tell how much of the song Rosa listened to.

SOLUTION

1 Draw equivalent number lines like those below. Label the endpoints and the halfway point on each number line. Locate and label 0.3 on the first number line.

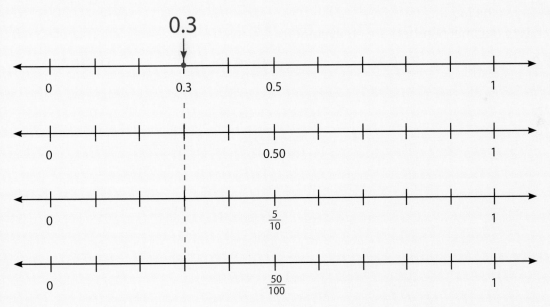

2 Draw a vertical line to locate one point on the decimal number line and one point on each of the fraction number lines that are lined up under 0.3. Then start at 0 and count by tenths or hundredths until you reach the vertical line at points 0.30, $\frac{3}{10}$, and $\frac{30}{100}$.

ANSWER The decimal number 0.30 and the fractions $\frac{3}{10}$ and $\frac{30}{100}$ are equivalent to 0.3.

L E A R N

Solve.

1. Johnny has many pets. $\frac{7}{10}$ of his pets are dogs. Write two equivalent decimal numbers and one equivalent fraction that tell how many of Johnny's pets are dogs.

2. A paintbrush is 0.4 in. wide. Write two equivalent fractions and one equivalent decimal number that tell the width of the paintbrush.

3. A block of cheese weighs $\frac{6}{10}$ pound. Write two decimal numbers that tell the weight of the cheese.

Choose the answer.

4. Which fraction is equivalent to 0.8?

   A. $\frac{0.8}{10}$ B. $\frac{8}{10}$ C. $\frac{0.8}{100}$ D. $\frac{8}{100}$

5. Which decimal number is equivalent to $\frac{42}{100}$?

   A. 0.42   B. 4.2   C. 42.0   D. 4.20

6. Which **two** decimal numbers are equivalent to $\frac{9}{10}$?

   A. 9.0   B. 0.9   C. 0.90   D. 90.0

Equivalent Decimals and Fractions

Fractions and Decimals — Same Value

Solve.

1. Bess walked $\frac{1}{10}$ mile to see her friend. Write three equivalent ways to tell how far Bess walked.

2. Gordon drove 0.8 of the distance from his house to the park. Write three equivalent ways to tell how much of the distance Gordon drove.

Choose the answer.

3. Which fraction is equivalent to 0.4?

   A. $\frac{0.4}{10}$ B. $\frac{4}{10}$

   C. $\frac{0.4}{100}$ D. $\frac{4}{100}$

4. Which **two** fractions are equivalent to 0.8?

   A. $\frac{0.8}{10}$ B. $\frac{0.80}{100}$

   C. $\frac{8}{10}$ D. $\frac{80}{100}$

5. Which decimal number is equivalent to $\frac{17}{100}$?

   A. 0.17   B. 1.7

   C. 17.0   D. 17.00

6. Which **two** decimal numbers are equivalent to $\frac{2}{10}$?

   A. 2.0   B. 0.2

   C. 20.0   D. 0.20

7. Which fraction is equivalent to 0.6?

   A. $\frac{0.6}{10}$ B. $\frac{0.6}{100}$

   C. $\frac{6}{10}$ D. $\frac{6}{100}$

8. Which decimal number is equivalent to $\frac{5}{10}$?

   A. 0.05   B. 0.5

   C. 5.0   D. 50.0

9. Which decimal number is equivalent to $\frac{23}{100}$?

   A. 0.0023   B. 0.023

   C. 0.23   D. 2.3

10. Which decimal number is equivalent to $\frac{33}{100}$?

   A. 0.33   B. 3.3

   C. 33.0   D. 330.0

11. Which **two** fractions are equivalent to 0.3?

   A. $\frac{0.3}{10}$ B. $\frac{3}{10}$

   C. $\frac{3}{100}$ D. $\frac{30}{100}$

12. Which **two** fractions are equivalent to 0.5?

   A. $\frac{5}{10}$ B. $\frac{0.5}{10}$

   C. $\frac{5}{100}$ D. $\frac{50}{100}$

13. Which **two** decimal numbers are equivalent to $\frac{7}{10}$?

   A. 0.7   B. 0.70

   C. 7.0   D. 70.0

14. Which decimal number is equivalent to $\frac{6}{100}$?

   A. 6.0   B. 0.06

   C. 0.6   D. 60.0

T R Y   I T

Halves and Fourths

Find Equivalent Fractions and Decimals

You can identify equivalent fractions and decimal numbers more than one way.
You can use what you know about money and you can use number lines.

PROBLEM Write a fraction and decimal that are both equivalent to 6.50.

SOLUTION 1

1 Use what you know about the value of a quarter to make a chart. There are 4 quarters in 1 dollar, so 1 quarter is one-fourth of a dollar, or $\frac{1}{4}$ of a dollar, or 0.25 of a dollar. Refer to the chart for equivalent values.

Number of Quarters	Decimal Equivalent	Fraction Equivalent
1 quarters	0.25	$\frac{1}{4}$
2 quarters	$0.50 = 0.5$	$\frac{2}{4} = \frac{1}{2}$
3 quarters	0.75	$\frac{3}{4}$
4 quarters	1.00	$\frac{4}{4}$

2 $6.50 = 6.5 = 6\frac{2}{4} = 6\frac{1}{2}$

SOLUTION 2

1 Draw number lines. Find a fraction and a decimal number that are located in the same position as 6.50.

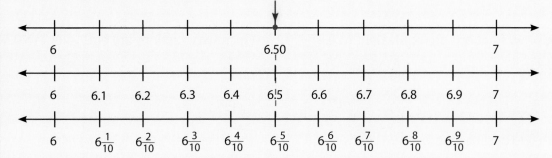

LEARN

2 Draw a vertical line to locate the two points on the second and third number lines that are exactly under 6.50. Both 6.5 and $6\frac{1}{2}$ are lined up under 6.50, so $6.50 = 6.5 = 6\frac{1}{2}$.

ANSWER 6.5 and $6\frac{1}{2}$ are equivalent to 6.50.

Solve.

1. Write a fraction and a decimal number that are both equivalent to $4\frac{1}{2}$.

2. Write a fraction and a decimal number that are both equivalent to $9\frac{1}{4}$.

Choose the answer.

3. Which fraction is equivalent to 0.25?

   A. $\frac{1}{4}$ B. $\frac{2}{5}$ C. $\frac{3}{4}$ D. $\frac{1}{10}$

4. Which fraction is equivalent to 4.75?

   A. $4\frac{1}{4}$ B. $3\frac{3}{4}$ C. $4\frac{7}{5}$ D. $4\frac{3}{4}$

5. Which decimal number is equivalent to $2\frac{1}{2}$?

   A. 2.1   B. 1.5   C. 2.5   D. 2.12

6. Which decimal number is equivalent to $8\frac{3}{4}$?

   A. 8.34   B. 8.25   C. 7.34   D. 8.75

7. Which **two** decimal numbers are equivalent to $3\frac{1}{2}$?

   A. 3.12   B. 3.5   C. 3.2   D. 3.50

8. Which **two** decimal numbers are equivalent to $\frac{1}{2}$?

   A. 1.2   B. 0.12   C. 0.5   D. 0.50

9. Which **two** fractions are equivalent to 4.75?

   A. $4\frac{5}{7}$ B. $4\frac{3}{4}$ C. $4\frac{9}{12}$ D. $4\frac{10}{12}$

10. Which **two** fractions are equivalent to 1.5?

    A. $1\frac{2}{4}$ B. $1\frac{3}{4}$ C. $1\frac{1}{5}$ D. $1\frac{3}{6}$

L E A R N

Relate Decimal Numbers to Fractions (B)

Decimal Numbers to Fractions

Write an equivalent fraction for the decimal number.

1. 0.75

2. 0.6

3. 0.2

4. 0.50

Read the problem and follow the directions.

5. Sketch a number line like the one shown. Put a dot on it to show the fraction $\frac{1}{2}$.

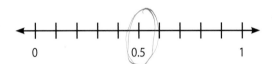

Choose the answer.

6. Which fraction is shown on this number line?

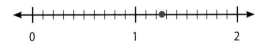

A. $1\frac{2}{10}$ B. $1\frac{1}{5}$

C. $1\frac{1}{4}$ D. $1\frac{3}{4}$

7. Which decimal number is shown on this number line?

A. 0.45   B. 0.8

C. 0.9   D. 0.5

8. Which shows a decimal equivalent to $2\frac{7}{10}$ on the number line?

A.

B.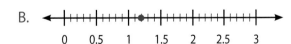

C.

D.

9. Which shows a fraction equivalent to 2.75 on the number line?

A.

B.

C.

D.

TRY IT

Probabilities as Fractions

Write a Probability as a Fraction

Worked Examples

You can write the probability of an event as 0 or 1 or as a fraction between 0 and 1.

A   B   C   D   E   F

PROBLEM 1   Use the letters above. What is the probability of choosing a vowel? Write your answer in simplest form.

SOLUTION   The vowels shown are A and E. There are 2 vowels out of a total of 6 letters. So the probability is 2 out of 6, or $\frac{2}{6} = \frac{1}{3}$.

ANSWER   The probability of choosing a vowel is $\frac{1}{3}$.

PROBLEM 2   Use the letters above. What is the probability of choosing a consonant? Write your answer in simplest form.

SOLUTION   The consonants shown are B, C, D, and F. There are 4 consonants out of a total of 6 letters. So the probability is 4 out of 6, or $\frac{4}{6} = \frac{2}{3}$.

ANSWER   The probability of choosing a consonant is $\frac{2}{3}$.

PROBLEM 3   Use the letters above. What is the probability of choosing a letter of the alphabet? Write your answer in simplest form.

SOLUTION   The letters shown are A, B, C, D, E, and F. There are 6 letters out of a total of 6 letters. So the probability is 6 out of 6, or $\frac{6}{6} = 1$.

ANSWER   The probability of choosing a letter is 1.

LEARN

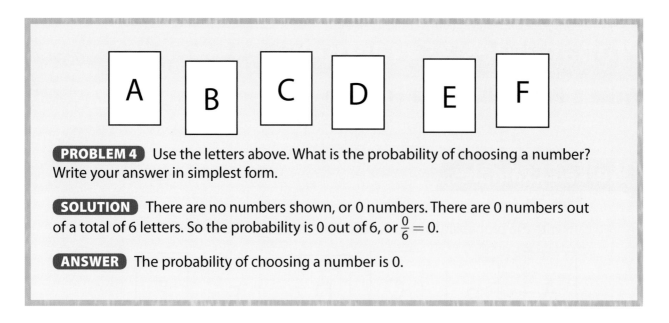

PROBLEM 4 Use the letters above. What is the probability of choosing a number? Write your answer in simplest form.

SOLUTION There are no numbers shown, or 0 numbers. There are 0 numbers out of a total of 6 letters. So the probability is 0 out of 6, or $\frac{0}{6} = 0$.

ANSWER The probability of choosing a number is 0.

Write the probability in words and as a fraction.

1. What is the probability that the spinner will land on a green section?

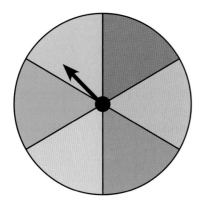

2. Tamara chooses a ball from a jar without looking. The jar contains 3 orange, 4 pink, 1 yellow, and 4 purple balls. What is the probability that Tamara will choose an orange ball?

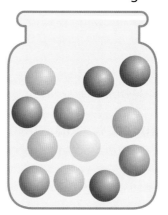

L E A R N

3. Mikel designed and colored a spinner so that the probability of the arrow landing on green is $\frac{1}{6}$. Which one of these spinners did Mikel make? Explain why the others could not be the spinner Mikel made.

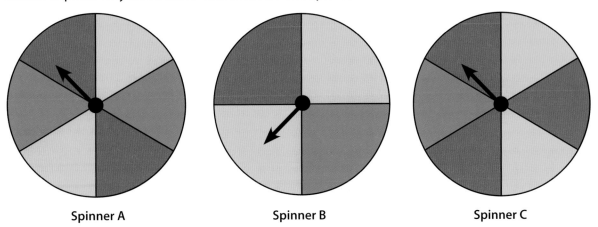

Spinner A   Spinner B   Spinner C

4. Olivia says that for each spinner, the probability of the spinner landing on blue is $\frac{1}{5}$. Is she correct? Explain your reasoning.

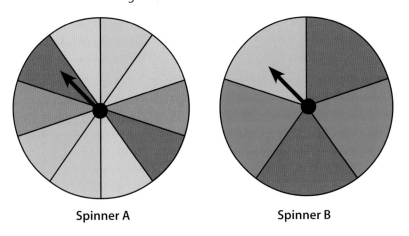

Spinner A   Spinner B

L E A R N

Organize Outcomes

Outcome Chart

Worked Examples

You can make an organized chart to show all the possible outcomes of an event happening in a probability experiment.

PROBLEM Winston tosses a number cube and a penny. The cube's sides are numbered 1, 2, 3, 4, 5, and 6. The penny can show either heads or tails. How many possible outcomes are there?

SOLUTION Make a chart to show all the possible outcomes of Winston's tosses. Then count all the possible outcomes, remembering that tossing a 3 and a heads, for example, is 1 outcome.

Number cube	Penny
1	H
1	T
2	H
2	T
3	H
3	T

Number cube	Penny
4	H
4	T
5	H
5	T
6	H
6	T

ANSWER There are 12 possible outcomes.

L E A R N

Complete the chart to solve the problem.

1. Marc has two fair spinners. One spinner has the numbers 1, 2, and 3 and the other has an equal number of red and blue sections. Marc spins both spinners. What are all the possible outcomes Marc could spin?

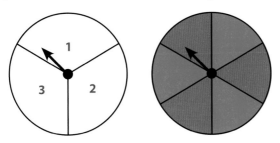

Number spinner	Color spinner
?	?
?	?
?	?
?	?
?	?
?	?

2. Tyler has a bag of letter tiles with the letters T, Y, L, E, R. Tyler reaches into the bag and chooses a letter. He then tosses a coin. What are all the possible outcomes of choosing a letter and tossing the coin? How many outcomes are there?

Letter	Coin
?	?
?	?
?	?
?	?
?	?
?	?
?	?
?	?
?	?
?	?

3. Wendy has three stacks of number cards. Each stack has equal numbers of 4s and 5s, and no other digits. Wendy randomly picks one card from each stack. On the chart below, list all the possible outcomes for the three cards Wendy picks. How many possible outcomes are there?

Stack 1	Stack 2	Stack 3
?	?	?
?	?	?
?	?	?
?	?	?
?	?	?
?	?	?
?	?	?
?	?	?

L E A R N

4. Jake tosses a number cube and spins a spinner. The number cube has the numbers 1, 2, 3, 4, 5, and 6. The spinner has the letters A, B, and C. What are the possible outcomes of tossing the number cube and spinning the spinner? How many outcomes are there?

Number cube	Spinner
?	?
?	?
?	?
?	?
?	?
?	?

Number cube	Spinner
?	?
?	?
?	?
?	?
?	?
?	?

Number cube	Spinner
?	?
?	?
?	?
?	?
?	?
?	?

134

Organize Outcomes

All Possible Outcomes

Read the problem and follow the directions.

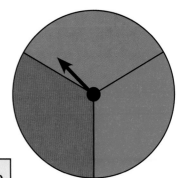

1. Miranda spins this spinner and tosses a fair number cube labeled 1, 2, 3, 4, 5, and 6.

   Make a chart to show all possible outcomes. Label the columns "Spinner" and "Number cube."

Spinner	Number cube
?	?
?	?
?	?
?	?
?	?
?	?
?	?
?	?
?	?

Spinner	Number cube
?	?
?	?
?	?
?	?
?	?
?	?
?	?
?	?
?	?

2. Jake decides to have the lunch combo at the deli. He can choose one sandwich, one side dish, and one drink.

   Draw a tree diagram to show all the possible lunches Jake could choose. How many possible lunch combinations are there?

Lunch Combo $7.99		
Sandwich	**Side**	**Drink**
roast beef	carrots	lemonade
veggie	apples	iced tea
chicken	chips	

TRY IT

3. Number Cube A has 1, 2, 3, 4, 5, and 6 on its sides. Number Cube B has 7, 8, 9, 10, 11, and 12 on its sides. List all the possible outcomes of tossing the two number cubes by completing the chart below.

Cube A	Cube B	Possible outcomes
1	?	?
	?	?
	?	?
	?	?
	?	?
	?	?
2	?	?
	?	?
	?	?
	?	?
	?	?
	?	?
3	?	?
	?	?
	?	?
	?	?
	?	?
	?	?

Cube A	Cube B	Possible outcomes
4	?	?
	?	?
	?	?
	?	?
	?	?
	?	?
5	?	?
	?	?
	?	?
	?	?
	?	?
	?	?
6	?	?
	?	?
	?	?
	?	?
	?	?
	?	?

TRY IT

Choose the answer.

4. Elki has a red sweater and a black sweater. She also has red pants and black pants. Which chart shows all possible combinations Elki could wear?

A.
	Red sweater	Black sweater
Red pants	RR	RB
Black pants	BR	BB

B.
	Red sweater	Black sweater
Red pants	RB	RB
Black pants	RB	RB

C.
	Red sweater	Black sweater
Red pants	RB	RB
Black pants	BR	BR

5. Rande has a tan hat and a white hat. He also has a blue shirt and a gray shirt. Which chart shows all possible combinations Rande could wear?

A.
	Tan hat	White hat
Blue shirt	BT	BW
Gray shirt	GT	GW

B.
	Tan hat	White hat
Blue shirt	BT	BB
Gray shirt	BT	BB

C.
	Tan hat	White hat
Blue shirt	BW	BW
Gray shirt	GW	GT

6. Pippa was baking some muffins. She baked either small or large muffins. She could bake either wheat or bran muffins. Which tree diagram shows all possible combinations of muffins Pippa could bake?

A.
large < wheat / small
small < bran / large

B.
large < wheat / bran
small < wheat / bran

C.
large < wheat / wheat
small < bran / bran

TRY IT

Find All Possible Combinations

Multiply to Find Combinations

You can make a tree diagram to show all the possible outcomes of an event happening in a probability experiment. To find the number of outcomes, you can count the outcomes or you can multiply.

PROBLEM Destiny has 3 sundresses, 2 pairs of sandals, and 2 hats. How many different combinations of 1 sundress, 1 pair of sandals, and 1 hat can she make?

SOLUTION 1 Make a tree diagram. Then count the number of outcomes listed in the far right column.

Dress	Shoes	Hat
	purple	tan / pink
yellow	red	tan / pink
	purple	tan / pink
pink	red	tan / pink
	purple	tan / pink
purple	red	tan / pink

—12

SOLUTION 2 Write a multiplication number sentence. Use the number of choices in each group as the factors in the number sentence. Solve.

$$3 \times 2 \times 2 = ?$$
$$3 \times 2 \times 2 = 12$$

Number of dresses		Number of sandal pairs		Number of hats		Number of outcomes
3	×	2	×	2	=	12

ANSWER 12; Destiny can make 12 different combinations.

LEARN

Write a number sentence to solve the problem. Then solve.

1. You are making sandwiches that each have one type of bread, one filling, and one dressing. How many different combinations of sandwiches can you make using white, rye, or wheat bread; ham, cheese, or turkey filling; and mayonnaise or mustard dressing?

2. Kurt wants to display one of each kind of model he has built. If he has 4 car models, 2 airplane models, and 2 ship models, how many different combinations of 1 car, 1 airplane, and 1 ship does he have?

3. The Diaz family will travel to Oregon, Arizona, or Nevada for vacation. They can drive or take a train, and they can go in June, July, August, or September. How many different combinations of vacations are possible?

4. Hannah is making indoor dish gardens for gifts. She has a begonia plant, a rose plant, and a bamboo plant. For planters, she has a tin container, a brass container, and a copper container, and she has three different types of soil. How many different combinations of indoor dish gardens are possible?

5. You toss a penny, choose a marble from a bag of 5 marbles each of a different color, and spin a spinner with equal yellow and purple sections. How many different outcomes are possible?

LEARN

Surveys

Survey Questions

You can conduct a survey to answer questions.

PROBLEM Look at the picture of the softball players. What question could you ask them to find out how many of these players wear hats to practice?

SOLUTION Write a question that could be answered Yes or No. If the question has too many possible answers, it will be difficult to analyze the data.

ANSWER Do you wear a hat to softball practice?

Use the photograph to complete Problems 1–4. Create a tally chart like the one shown to record your questions and answers.

1. Write two Yes or No survey questions you could ask to find out how many of these players are on each team. Use the photograph to answer the questions.

2. Write two Yes or No survey questions you could ask to find out what color uniform, purple or green, the player's team wears. Use the photograph to answer the questions.

3. Write one Yes or No survey question you could ask to find out how many players like to play outfield. Imagine how the players would answer.

4. What other information could you gather from the players? Write two Yes or No survey questions you could ask to gather this information. Imagine how the players would answer.

Softball Survey				
Survey question	Tally: Yes	Frequency: Yes	Tally: No	Frequency: No
?	?	?	?	?
?	?	?	?	?
?	?	?	?	?
?	?	?	?	?
?	?	?	?	?
?	?	?	?	?
?	?	?	?	?

Surveys

Represent Data

Worked Examples

You can make graphs to show many types of data, including survey data.

PROBLEM 1 Make a line graph to show these survey data.

Daily High Temperatures

Mon. – 75°F	Thurs. – 80°F	Sat. – 82°F
Tues. – 65°F	Fri. – 85°F	Sun. – 75°F
Wed. – 60°F		

SOLUTION Write the title "Daily High Temperatures" for the line graph. Decide on an appropriate scale to show the temperatures. Show the scale on the vertical axis (*y*-axis) and label the axis "Temperature (°F)." Write each day of the week on the horizontal axis (*x*-axis) and label the axis "Day." Make a point to show the temperature for each day and connect the points with line segments.

ANSWER

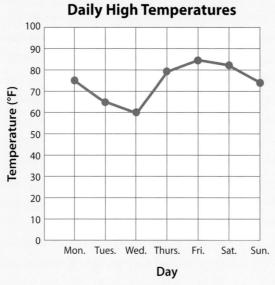

LEARN

PROBLEM 2 Make a line plot to show these survey data.

Age of Players on Marisa's Softball Team

Marisa – 9	Linda – 9	Pamela – 12
Tina – 12	Courtney – 8	Eve – 9
Jackie – 10	Jessie – 11	Erin – 11
Lisa – 11	Val – 10	Jill – 9

SOLUTION Write the title "Age of Players on Marisa's Softball Team" for the line plot. Then group the ages of the players. Draw a scale for the ages along a number line and label it "Age (years)." For each player, draw an X above the number that represents that player's age.

ANSWER **Age of Players on Marisa's Softball Team**

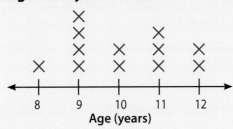

PROBLEM 3 Make a horizontal bar graph to show these survey data.

Favorite Sport

Baseball – 10 votes	Soccer – 8 votes
Basketball – 5 votes	Tennis – 4 votes

SOLUTION Write the title "Favorite Sport" for the bar graph. List the sports on the vertical axis (*y*-axis) and label the axis "Sport." Decide on an appropriate scale to show the number of votes. Show the scale on the horizontal axis (*x*-axis) and label the axis "Votes." Draw a bar for each sport to show the number of votes along the *x*-axis. Leave space between each two bars.

ANSWER

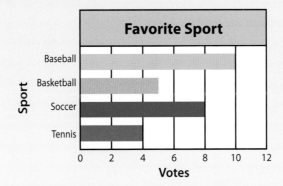

L E A R N

PROBLEM 4 Make a vertical double bar graph to show these survey data.

Softball Scores at Harper's Field

	Game 1	Game 2	Game 3	Game 4
Home	8	5	7	6
Visitor	6	9	6	10

SOLUTION Write the title "Softball Scores" for the bar graph. Decide on an appropriate scale to show the number of runs scored. Show the scale on the vertical axis (y-axis) and label the axis "Runs scored." List the games on the horizontal axis (x-axis) and label the axis "Games." Make a legend for Home and Visitors. For each game, draw two bars that touch and show the number of runs on the y-axis. Leave space between each pair of bars.

ANSWER

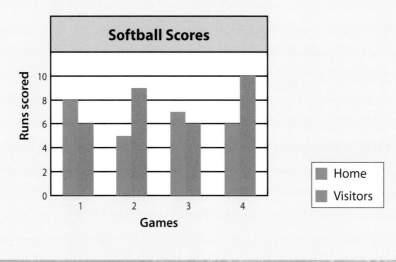

Show the data as directed by the problem.

1. The coach recorded the number of goals scored by players on the soccer team this season.

Mark – 4 goals	Tori – 3 goals
Jeff – 5 goals	Finn – 2 goals
Billy – 2 goals	Hank – 4 goals
Kyle – 2 goals	Miley – 2 goals
Wendy – 1 goal	Adam – 1 goal

   Make a line plot to show the data.

2. Nicole asked 11 people, "What is your favorite exercise?"
5 people said bicycling, 2 people said swimming, and 4 people said running.
Make a bar graph to show the data.

3. Tyler's mom recorded his height as he grew.

> Birth – 23 inches
> Age 2 – 34 inches
> Age 4 – 40 inches
> Age 6 – 46 inches

Make a line graph to show the data.

4. The ticket booth at the stadium recorded the number of adult and child
tickets sold for the first three games of the season.

> Game 1 – 350 adult tickets, 120 child tickets
> Game 2 – 325 adult tickets, 150 child tickets
> Game 3 – 400 adult tickets, 200 child tickets

Make a double bar graph to show the data.

Surveys

Data Collection

Read the problem and follow the directions.

1. Matthew is planning to have his teammates over for dinner after Saturday's baseball game. Write a survey question he could ask to help him decide what food to serve.

2. Lily asked boys and girls at Moore Park, "What is your favorite thing about the park?" 15 boys and 10 girls said the hiking trails, 10 boys and 16 girls said the playground, 13 boys and 8 girls said the basketball courts, and 6 boys and 8 girls said the picnic area. Make a double bar graph to show the data.

Choose the answer.

3. Dylan wants to survey his friends to find out which breed of dog they like best. Which question should Dylan ask?

   A. What breed of dog do you have?

   B. What is your favorite breed of dog?

   C. Which breed of dog has the longest fur?

   D. What is your favorite type of pet?

4. Sofia wants to survey her neighbors to find out their thoughts about putting a stop sign on their corner. Which question should Sofia ask?

   A. How many stop signs should we have on our street?

   B. Do you prefer stop signs or yield signs?

   C. Do you want a stop sign on this corner?

   D. Do you always stop at stop signs?

TRY IT

5. Latanya asked 12 people, "What is your favorite vacation?"
   Which tally chart correctly shows this information?

Jeff – visiting relatives   Gregg – going to a theme park
Amiel – camping   Cindy – visiting relatives
Gordon – visiting relatives   Marita – camping
Theresa – going to a theme park   Craig – visiting relatives
Emily – visiting relatives   Suketu – camping
Akiko – visiting relatives   Tim – visiting relatives

A.

Favorite Vacations

Vacation	Tally
Camping	|||
Visiting relatives	~~||||~~ ||
Going to a theme park	||

B.

Favorite Vacations

Vacation	Tally
Camping	||||
Visiting relatives	~~||||~~ ||
Going to a theme park	||

C.

Favorite Vacations

Vacation	Tally
Camping	|||
Visiting relatives	~~||||~~	
Going to a theme park	|||

D.

Favorite Vacations

Vacation	Tally
Camping	||
Visiting relatives	~~||||~~ |||
Going to a theme park	||

6. Marie asked 12 people, "What is your favorite pizza topping?"
   Which tally chart correctly shows this information?

Riva – mushroom	Marcos – pineapple
Nina – pepperoni	Diego – pepperoni
Mike – pineapple	Lisa – sausage
Sean – pepperoni	Amanda – mushroom
Josh – pepperoni	Terry – olive
Gema – sausage	Ana – pepperoni

A.

Favorite Pizza Topping

Topping	Tally
Mushroom	I
Olive	II
Pepperoni	|||||
Pineapple	II
Sausage	II

B.

Favorite Pizza Topping

Topping	Tally
Mushroom	|||||
Olive	I
Pepperoni	II
Pineapple	II
Sausage	II

C.

Favorite Pizza Topping

Topping	Tally
Mushroom	II
Olive	II
Pepperoni	|||||
Pineapple	I
Sausage	II

D.

Favorite Pizza Topping

Topping	Tally
Mushroom	II
Olive	I
Pepperoni	|||||
Pineapple	II
Sausage	II

TRY IT

7. Diana recorded the amount of time she spent reading her book each day for a week.

Sunday – 15 minutes	Wednesday – 20 minutes	Saturday – 25 minutes
Monday – 25 minutes	Thursday – 30 minutes	
Tuesday – 15 minutes	Friday – 15 minutes	

Which line plot correctly shows this information?

A.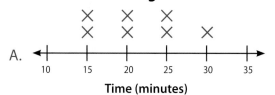

B.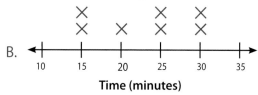

C.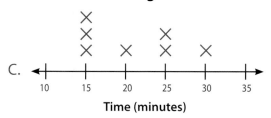

D.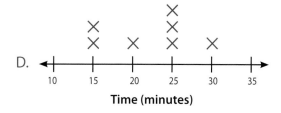

8. Tony wanted to graph these data.

> Jill weighs 88 pounds and is 48 inches tall.
> Bob weighs 82 pounds and is 53 inches tall.
> Nadia weighs 91 pounds and is 52 inches tall.
> Gregg weighs 85 pounds and is 50 inches tall.
> Kenta weighs 78 pounds and is 50 inches tall.
> Sumi weighs 80 pounds and is 48 inches tall.
> Marco weighs 78 pounds and is 51 inches tall.
> Anne weighs 75 pounds and is 54 inches tall.

Which is the best scale to use when graphing this information
on a double bar graph?

A. 1 row = 1 unit

B. 1 row = 10 units

C. 1 row = 50 units

D. 1 row = 100 units

TRY IT

9. The cashier at the zoo recorded the number of adults and children who bought tickets over the long weekend.

Saturday – 150 adults, 225 children
Sunday – 175 adults, 200 children
Monday – 150 adults, 275 children

Which double bar graph correctly shows this information?

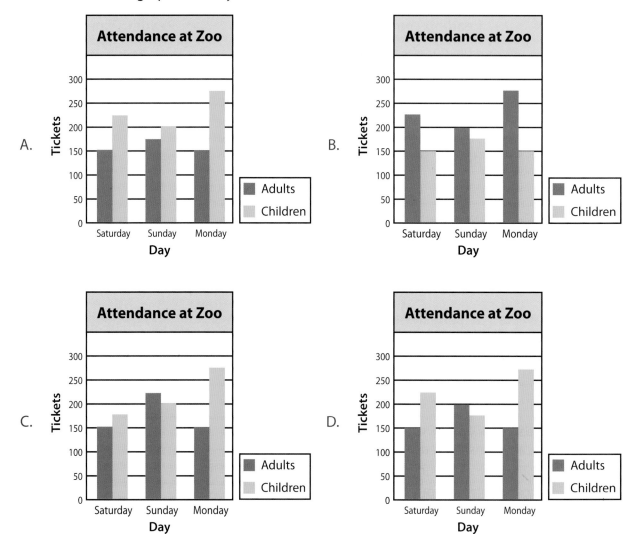

TRY IT

10. Tayton recorded the total runs scored by his team after each inning of the baseball game.

Inning 1 – 0 runs	Inning 4 – 3 runs	Inning 7 – 9 runs
Inning 2 – 2 runs	Inning 5 – 8 runs	Inning 8 – 9 runs
Inning 3 – 2 runs	Inning 6 – 8 runs	Inning 9 – 9 runs

Which line graph correctly shows this information?

A.

B.
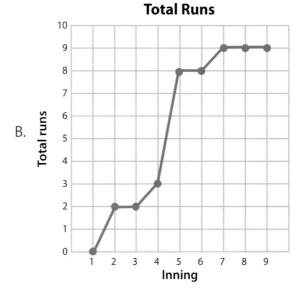

C.
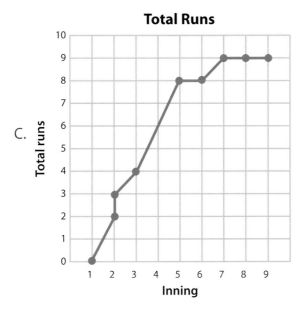

D.
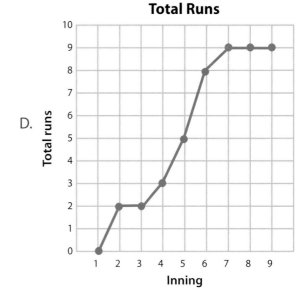

11. Carlos recorded the number of each type of insect he saw at the park.

Insects	
Ant	‖‖‖ ‖‖‖ ‖‖‖ ‖‖‖
Fly	‖‖‖ ‖
Bee	‖‖‖ ‖‖‖ ‖‖
Butterfly	‖‖‖ ‖
Ladybug	‖‖‖‖

Which bar graph correctly shows this information?

A.
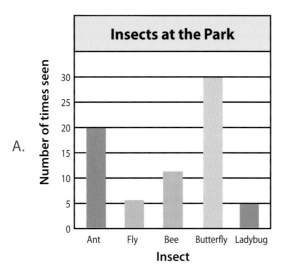

B.
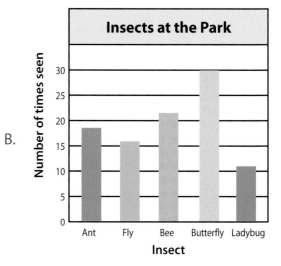

C.
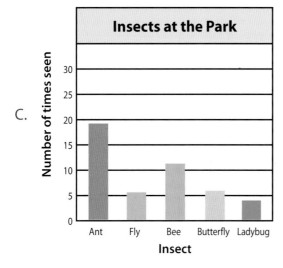

D.
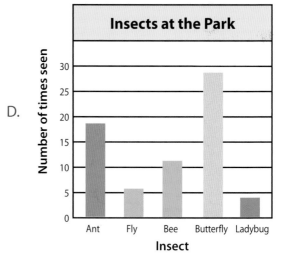

TRY IT

Data Representations

The Best Data Display

When you have data to display, use the type of graph that best represents the data. Also be sure that your graph has a title, a scale, axis labels, and if necessary, a legend.

PROBLEM For Arbor Day in 2003, Marcus planted a tree in his backyard. Each year he measures the height of the tree and records the data in his notebook. He has made this line graph to display data he has collected.

2003: 32 inches
2004: 40 inches
2005: 47 inches
2006: 58 inches
2007: 64 inches
2008: 70 inches
2009: 72 inches

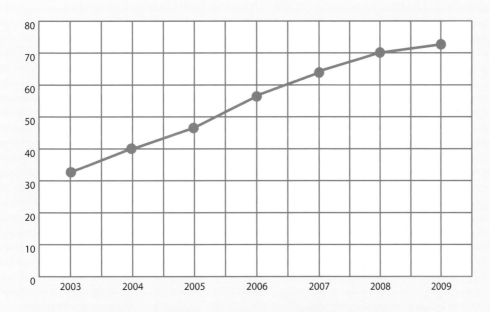

What information is missing from the graph? Fill in the information that is missing. Then explain why the line graph is a good choice for displaying this data.

L E A R N

1 Check to see that the graph has the following parts:

- Title? No
- Scale? Yes
- Axis labels? No
- Legend? You don't need a legend because the graph only has one line.

2 Decide what the vertical axis (*y*-axis) represents. Write a label.

3 Decide what the horizontal axis (*x*-axis) represents. Write a label.

4 Read the problem again. Write a title.

ANSWER The title and labels for the axes are missing. The label for the *y*-axis could be "Height (inches)." The label for the *x*-axis could be "Year." The title for the graph could be "Height and Growth of Marcus's Tree." The line graph is a good choice because it shows change over time.

Read the problem and follow the directions.

1. Tom collected data about the amount of money children charge to wash cars. He wants to compare the amounts that the children charge, so he created the bar graph shown. Fill in the information that is missing from the bar graph. Explain why the bar graph is a good choice for displaying these data.

Name	Amount	Name	Amount	Name	Amount	Name	Amount
Jackson	$10	Shelly	$8	Aislin	$8	Mark	$8
Alice	$8	Ralph	$7	Maggie	$10	Ivy	$3

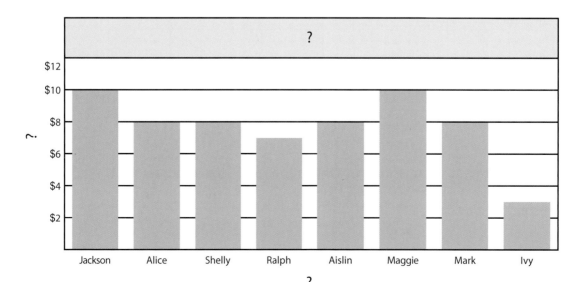

2. Gregory collected data about the number of sunny days each month.

Month	# of Days
January	17
February	16
March	17
April	18
May	20
June	25
July	27
August	26
September	23
October	20
November	18
December	16

On the next page are three ways to display the data.
Which data display do you think best shows the data?
Explain your answer.

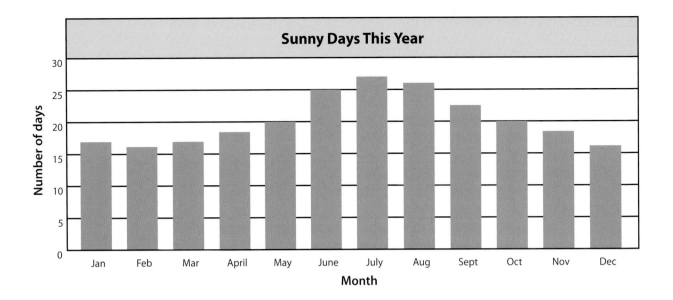

Sunny Days This Year

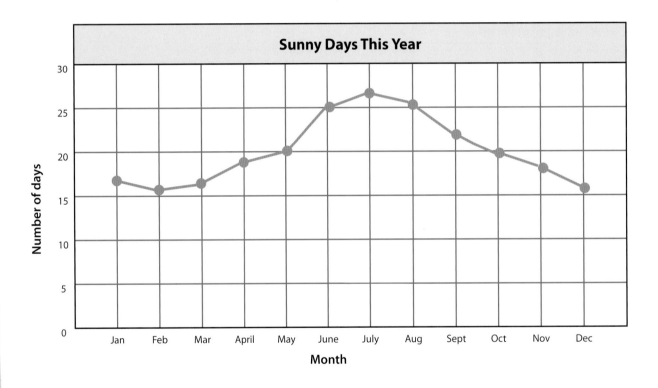

Sunny Days This Year

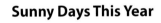
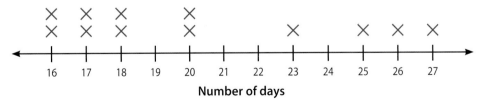

Choose the answer.

3. Louise collected the following data about the favorite colors of some boys and girls.

Color	# of boys	# of girls	Color	# of boys	# of girls
Orange	50	49	Green	27	13
Purple	34	21	Red	3	19

Which data display best represents the data?

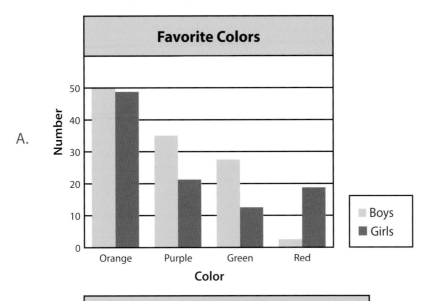

A.

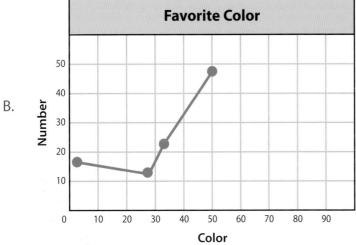

B.

C.

L E A R N

4. Halle collected the following data about the number of miles she ran each day.

Day	# of miles	Day	# of miles	Day	# of miles	Day	# of miles
Day 1	4	Day 3	4	Day 5	3	Day 7	5
Day 2	6	Day 4	2	Day 6	4		

Which data display best shows the number of miles that occurs most often?

A.

Day 1	||||	Day 5	|||
Day 2	||||		Day 6	||||
Day 3	|||||	Day 7	||||
Day 4	||		

B.

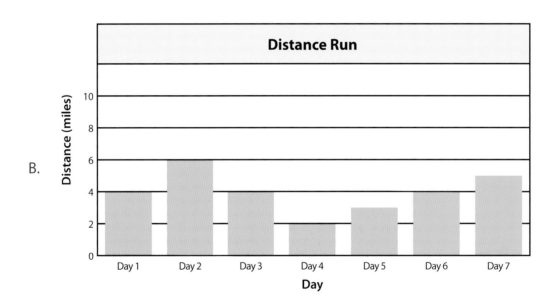

C.

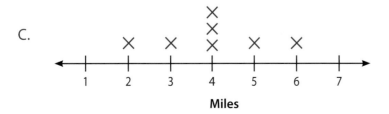

LEARN

Data Representations

Data Display Selection

Choose the answer.

1. Chelsea collected the following data about the number of days that it rained each month.

Month	# of Days	Month	# of Days	Month	# of Days
January	3	May	6	September	1
February	5	June	3	October	3
March	3	July	no rain	November	5
April	3	August	2	December	3

Which data display best represents the data?

A.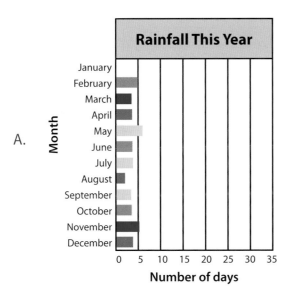

B.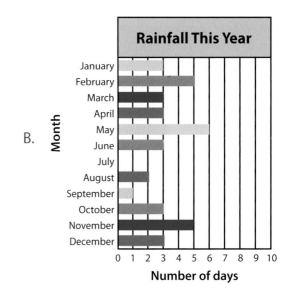

C.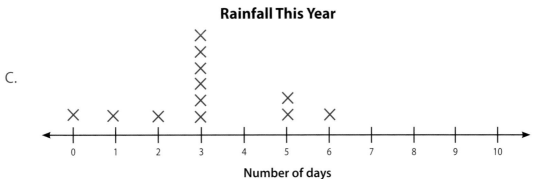

TRY IT

2. Jenelle collected the following data about the number of boys and girls playing different sports.

Sport	# of boys	# of girls	Sport	# of boys	# of girls
Soccer	53	49	Ice hockey	27	13
Baseball	34	21	Field hockey	3	19

Which graph best represents the data?

A.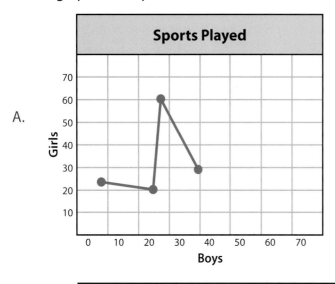

B.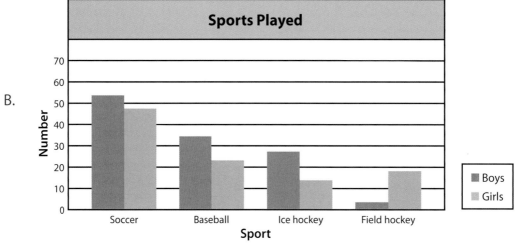

C.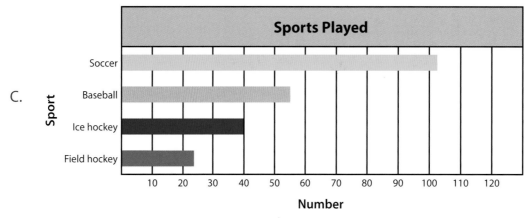

160

3. Tom collected the following data about the amount other children were charging to wash cars.

Name	Amount	Name	Amount	Name	Amount	Name	Amount
Jackson	$10	Shelly	$8	Aislin	$8	Mark	$8
Alice	$8	Ralph	$7	Maggie	$10	Ivy	$3

Which data display is used to show the amount that occurs most often?

Amount Charged to Wash Cars

A.

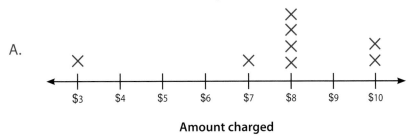

Amount charged

B.

Jackson	卌 卌	Aislin	卌 |||
Alice	卌 |||	Maggie	卌 卌
Shelly	卌 |||	Mark	卌 |||
Ralph	卌 ||	Ivy	|||

TRY IT

4. Kent wanted to know if he would do better on tests if he spent more time doing his homework. Kent collected the following data.

Subject	Time	Score	Subject	Time	Score	Subject	Time	Score
Math	30 min	10	Math	10 min	5	Reading	15 min	7
Spelling	15 min	6	Math	20 min	7	Spelling	15 min	5
Math	25 min	8	Spelling	25 min	9			

Which data display will best show this information?

A.
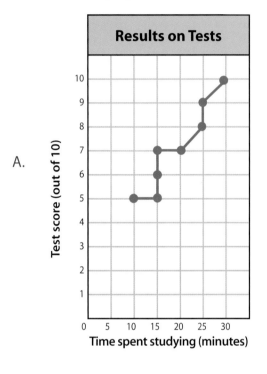

B.
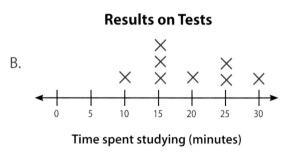

C.
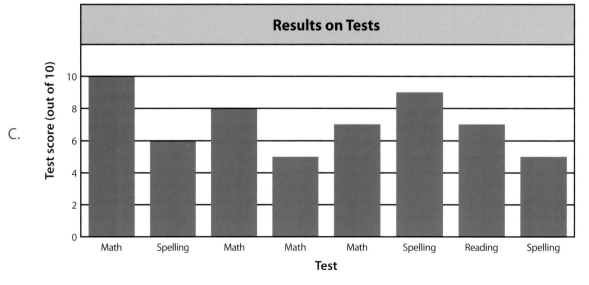

TRY IT

5. Gina wanted to know if her sunflowers would grow taller if she gave them more water. Gina collected the following data.

Water	Growth	Water	Growth
10 mL	2 cm	15 mL	4 cm
5 mL	1 cm	10 mL	3 cm
20 mL	5 cm		

Which data display will best show this information?

A.

10 mL of water	||
5 mL of water	|
20 mL of water	卌
15 mL of water	||||
10 mL of water	|||

B.

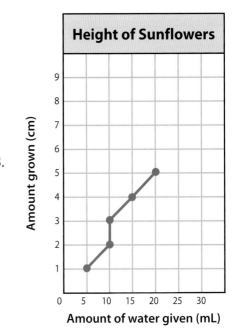

C.

Height of Sunflowers

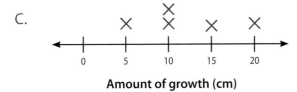

Amount of growth (cm)

Analyze Story Problems (B)

Use a Problem-Solving Plan

Worked Examples

You can use a 4-step problem-solving plan to solve a story problem. When you solve a multistep problem, you can break it into simpler parts.

PROBLEM Hannah is at a choir concert. The choir sings 5 songs that are each about 3 minutes long. The choir stands in two different sections with 6 rows in each section. In the first section, there are 5 members in each row. In the second section, there are 6 members in each row. Three-fifths of the choir members are girls. The rest are boys. How many members are there in the choir?

SOLUTION

UNDERSTAND THE PROBLEM You need to find out how many members there are in the choir. First you need to find out how many members stand in each of the sections.

You do **not** need to know how many songs the choir sings, how long each song is, or how many choir members are girls or boys.

DEVISE A PLAN

❶ Find the number of choir members that stand in the first section.

❷ Find the number of choir members that stand in the second section.

❸ Write a number sentence to find the total number of choir members that stand in both sections. Then solve.

CARRY OUT THE PLAN

❶ There are 6 rows in the first section. 5 choir members stand in each row. Multiply 6 rows by 5 choir members per row.
$6 \times 5 = 30$; 30 choir members

❷ There are 6 rows in the second section. 6 choir members stand in each row. Multiply 6 rows by 6 choir members per row.
$6 \times 6 = 36$; 36 choir members

❸ $30 + 36 = ?$
30 choir members + 36 choir members = 66 choir members

LOOK BACK Make sure you've answered the question that was asked. You can use opposite operations, or inverse operations, to check your work.

- Does 6 rows × 5 choir members = 30 choir members?
  Yes, because 30 ÷ 5 = 6.

- Does 6 rows × 6 choir members = 36 choir members?
  Yes, because 36 ÷ 6 = 6.

- Does 30 + 36 = 66 choir members?
  Yes, because 66 − 36 = 30.

So the correct answer is 66 choir members.

ANSWER There are 66 members in the choir.

Solve. Use the problem-solving plan; show how you looked back to check your answer.

1. Stephen is planning a party for 13 people. Everyone will have 30 minutes to eat dinner. He will serve pizza. 1 pizza feeds 6 people. During the party, he wants to play 3 games. 2 of the games will take 15 minutes each. 1 game will take 20 minutes. He will give each guest 2 party favors. Stephen will start the activities of the party 10 minutes after it starts to give all his guests a chance to arrive. Stephen wants his party to end at 8:00 p.m.

   At what time should Stephen's party start?

2. Yolanda, Jerry, and Sarah collect trading cards. A card box holds 35 cards. A card album holds 40 cards. Yolanda has 45 cards. Jerry has an album full of cards. Sarah has two full boxes of cards.

   How many more cards would Yolanda have to get to have the same number of cards as Sarah?

L E A R N

Analyze Story Problems (B)

Solve Problems

Explain the steps to solve the problem.

1. The baker used 52 cups of white flour, 13 cups of wheat flour, and 7 cups of sugar every day.

   How much flour did the baker use in 5 days?

Identify the information that is necessary to solve the problem.

2. Margaret curls up on the sofa and reads for 30 minutes and then plays outside for 45 minutes on Saturday and 45 minutes on Sunday.

   For how many minutes does Margaret play outside on the weekend?

Choose the plan that solves the problem.

3. Sarah is assembling 1 bag for each of 7 participants in a competition. She puts 2 shirts and 12 pins in each bag. In each bag she also puts 3 instructions packets.

   How many shirts and pins did Sarah put in the bags altogether?

   A. Add the number of shirts in each bag to 7. Add the number of pins in each bag to 7. Then add those sums.

   B. Add the number of shirts in each bag to the number of pins in each bag. Multiply that sum by 7.

   C. Multiply the number of shirts in each bag by 7. Multiply the number of pins in each bag by 3. Then add those products.

4. Solei washed 3 loads of laundry on the weekend and 2 loads of laundry during the week. Each load takes 35 minutes to wash and uses 5 gallons of water per load.

   How much water did Solei use to do his laundry?

   A. **Step 1:** Add $3 + 2$.
      Step 2: Multiply the sum by 35.

   B. **Step 1:** Add $3 + 2$.
      Step 2: Multiply the sum by 5.

   C. **Step 1:** Multiply 3×5.
      Step 2: Add 35 to the product.

   D. **Step 1:** Multiply 2×35.
      Step 2: Add 5 to the product.

TRY IT

Multistep Problems

Solve Multistep Problems

Worked Examples

You can use the problem-solving plan to solve a story problem. To solve a multistep problem, you can break it into simpler parts.

PROBLEM Mr. Zimmer is building steps to his porch. He needs 4 boards that are 12 feet long. He needs 6 boards that are 18 feet long. How many feet of board does Mr. Zimmer need in all?

SOLUTION

UNDERSTAND THE PROBLEM You need to find out how many total feet of board Mr. Zimmer needs to build the steps. First, find out how many feet are in four 12-foot-long boards and in six 18-foot-long boards.

DEVISE A PLAN Break this multistep problem into simpler parts.

1 Find the number of feet in four 12-foot-long boards.

2 Find the number of feet in six 18-foot-long boards.

3 Write a number sentence to find the total number of feet of board Mr. Zimmer needs. Then solve.

CARRY OUT THE PLAN

1 There are 4 boards. Each board is 12 feet long.
Multiply 4 boards by 12 feet per board.
$4 \times 12 = 48$; 48 feet

2 There are 6 boards. Each board is 18 feet long.
Multiply 6 boards by 18 feet per board.
$6 \times 18 = 108$; 108 feet

3 $48 + 108 = ?$
48 feet $+$ 108 feet $=$ 156 feet

LOOK BACK Make sure you've answered the question that was asked. Estimate the answer, about 150 feet (50 feet $+$ 100 feet $=$ 150 feet.) Since 156 feet is close to the estimate of 150 feet, the answer makes sense.

ANSWER Mr. Zimmer needs 156 feet of board.

L E A R N

Use this story problem to solve Problems 1 and 2.

Katie is having a party. She wants to tape paper streamers from the ceiling. Each red streamer is 6 feet long and each yellow streamer is 7 feet long. If Katie hangs 10 red streamers and 7 yellow streamers, how many feet of paper streamers will she use altogether?

1. What are the simpler parts of the problem?

2. What is the answer to the problem?

Use this story problem to solve Problems 3 and 4.

Josh needs to buy 4 cans of paint. Al's Paint and Go sells paint for $11.50 a can. Bob's Paint Shop sells paint for $22 for 2 cans. Mazzeo's Paint and Stuff sells paint for $48 for 4 cans. At which store is the paint the least expensive? How much will Josh save by buying the paint at that store rather than either of the other two stores?

3. What are the simpler parts of the problem?

4. What is the answer to the problem?

Use this story problem to solve Problems 5 and 6.

Tyson and Jonathan go to the Snack Shack for lunch. Tyson buys a special, a chef salad, and a large drink. Jonathan buys two specials. Who spends more? How much more?

5. What are the simpler parts of the problem?

6. What is the answer to the problem?

Menu	
Chef Salad	$5.50
Hamburger	$4.25
Hot Dog	$3.75
Chicken Sandwich	$4.50

Drink
  small
  medium
  large
	$0.75
	$1.15
	$1.25

Chips	$1.00
Special = 1 meal + medium drink + chips	$6.50

LEARN

Estimate to Predict and Verify (A)
Estimate with Mental Math

Worked Examples

You can estimate to solve a story problem that does not require an exact answer.

PROBLEM Last week a 747 jet airliner made 18 flights with no empty seats. If each flight carried 222 passengers, about how many passengers did the airliner carry last week?

SOLUTION

UNDERSTAND THE PROBLEM The question is, "About how many passengers did the airliner carry last week?" So the answer should be an estimate, not an exact solution.

DEVISE A PLAN You need to break the problem into three parts. Use friendly numbers to round. Use mental math to solve.

1 Round the number of flights to the nearest ten.

2 Round the number of passengers per flight to the nearest hundred.

3 Write a number sentence to multiply the estimated number of flights × the estimated number of passengers. Then solve.

CARRY OUT THE PLAN

1 Round 18 flights to 20 flights.

2 Round 222 passengers to 200 passengers.

3 $20 \times 200 = ?$
$20 \times 200 = 4,000$; The airliner carried about 4,000 passengers last week.

LOOK BACK Reread the problem to be sure you answered the question. Use a number line or place-value chart to be sure you rounded correctly. Then use the inverse operation of division to check your calculation. Does $4,000 \div 20 = 200$? Yes.

ANSWER The airliner carried about 4,000 passengers.

LEARN

Write a number sentence you can use to estimate the answer. Then solve.

1. Last week a 747 jet airliner made 9 flights with no empty seats. If 1,998 passengers flew on the jet last week, about how many passengers were on each flight?

2. A flower shop has 4,867 carnations to tie in bunches with 7 carnations in each bunch. About how many bunches of carnations will the flower shop have?

3. The best tickets to one New York City play cost $288 each. If 42 people buy those tickets, about how much money will the box office collect for the best tickets?

4. During the first week of the county fair, 19,793 people attended the fair. During the second week of the fair, 13,123 attended. About how many people attended the county fair during its first two weeks?

5. During the first two weeks of the county fair, 23,028 people used student passes and 9,888 people used paid tickets. About how many more people used student passes than paid tickets?

LEARN

Estimate to Predict and Verify (A)

Estimation with Story Problems

Read the problem and follow the directions.

1. In 2009, the population of a small city was 45,925.
   If the population were to decrease by 1,099 people in the next
   5 years, what would the population be in 2014?

   Use estimation to predict the answer to the nearest thousand.

Choose the answer.

2. A stamp collector has 1,176 stamps from 6 different countries.
   He has an equal number of stamps from each country.
   How many stamps does the stamp collector have from each country?

   Which estimation can you use to estimate the answer to the story problem?

   A. $1,800 \div 6$　　　　　　　　　　B. $1,200 \div 6$

   C. $1,200 \div 5$　　　　　　　　　　D. $1,299 \times 6$

3. A bird-watching club has an outing once a year. The members counted
   469 birds the first year, 613 birds the second year, and 545 birds the
   third year. A student answered that the club saw 1,627 birds in the
   3 years of bird-watching outings.

   Which statement about the student's answer is correct?

   A. The answer should be about 1,600. The student's answer is not correct.

   B. The answer should be about 1,500. The student's answer is correct.

   C. The answer should be about 15,000. The student's answer is not correct.

   D. The answer should be about 16,000. The student's answer is not correct.

4. A theater group sold tickets for 29 days before the performance.
   If the group sold 87 tickets each day, about how many tickets
   did the members sell in the 29 days?

   Which answer will give the most accurate estimation?

   A. $90 + 30$　　　　　　　　　　B. 80×30

   C. $90 \div 30$　　　　　　　　　　D. 90×30

Estimate to Predict and Verify (B)

Analyze and Solve Story Problems

You can estimate the answer to a story problem. Then you can solve the problem and compare your exact answer to your estimate. If the two values are close, then your answer is reasonable.

PROBLEM   An office building with 8 floors has 39 lamps on each floor. Each lamp holds 1 light bulb. The building owner is replacing old light bulbs with energy-saving bulbs. So far, she has replaced 53 bulbs. How many bulbs does she still need to replace?

SOLUTION

UNDERSTAND THE PROBLEM   You need to find out how many light bulbs the building manager still needs to replace after she replaces 53 bulbs. But first you need to find out how many total lamps are in the building.

DEVISE A PLAN   This is a multistep problem. You need to break the problem into three parts.

1   Estimate the answer to the story problem.

2   Find the number of lamps, each needing 1 light bulb.

3   Write a number sentence to subtract 53 from the total number of lamps. Then solve.

CARRY OUT THE PLAN

1   Round 39 to 40. There are about 40 lamps on each floor. There are 8 floors. Use mental math to multiply $40 \times 8 = 320$. So you know there are about 320 lamps in all. Round 53 to 50. About 50 bulbs have been replaced.
$320 - 50 = ?$; $320 - 50 = 270$; About 270 light bulbs still need to be replaced

2   There are 39 lamps on each floor with 1 bulb in each lamp. $39 \times 1 = 39$
There are 8 floors with 39 bulbs to replace on each floor. $8 \times 39 = 312$
So there are 312 lamps in the building.

3 $312 - 53 = ?$; $312 - 53 = 259$

LEARN

LOOK BACK Compare the exact answer to the estimate. Since an answer of 259 light bulbs is fairly close to the estimate of 270 light bulbs, then the answer is reasonable but should be checked again for accuracy.

ANSWER The building manager still needs to replace 259 light bulbs.

Estimate the answer, and then solve. Use the estimate to explain why the answer is reasonable.

1. How many yards of rope are needed to make eighteen 6-foot jump ropes and thirty-one 9-foot jump ropes? There are 3 feet in 1 yard.

   Estimate?
   Exact answer?
   Explanation?

2. A farmer has 9 cartons of potatoes. Each carton weighs 59 pounds. If all the potatoes are about the same weight and size, how many 3-pound bags of potatoes can the farmer make?

   Estimate?
   Exact answer?
   Explanation?

3. A restaurant has 19 inside tables that can each seat 6 people . It has 11 outside tables that can each seat 4 people. How many total people can be seated inside and outside the restaurant?

   Estimate?
   Exact answer?
   Explanation?

L E A R N

Estimate to Predict and Verify (B)

Solve Problems with Data from Tables

Worked Examples

You can solve story problems with data from tables. You can compare your exact answer to an estimate, or prediction, to be sure your answer is reasonable.

PROBLEM Steve buys 93 bags of doggie treats. He repackages them in 9-ounce portions. How many portions will he have?

Treats	Price
Doggie Treat 21 oz bag	$3.80

SOLUTION

UNDERSTAND THE PROBLEM The problem is asking how many 9-ounce portions of doggie treats Steve will have.

DEVISE A PLAN This is a multistep problem. Break the problem into three parts. Use the information in the table to solve one or more of the parts.

1 Make a written estimate.

2 Find the number of ounces of doggie treats that Steve has in all.

3 Write a number sentence to divide the total ounces of doggie treats into 9-ounce portions. Then solve.

CARRY OUT THE PLAN

1 Round 93 to 90. Steve buys about 90 bags of treats.
Round 21 to 20. Each bag holds about 20 ounces of treats.
90×20 ounces $= 1,800$; Steve has about 1,800 ounces of treats in all.
Each portion is 9 ounces. Mentally divide $1,800 \div 9 = 200$.
Estimate: Steve has about 200 portions.

2 Each bag has 21 ounces of treats.
93×21 ounces $= 1,953$ ounces

3 $1,953$ ounces $\div 9 = ?$; $1,953$ ounces $\div 9 = 217$; Exact answer: 217 bags

LOOK BACK Compare the estimate to the exact answer. The exact answer of 217 bags is close to the estimate of 200 bags, so it is a reasonable answer.

ANSWER Steve can make 217 bags of doggie treats.

LEARN

Use the tables to solve. First write the estimate. Then write the exact answer.

Dog gates	Sale price
77-inch flexible gate	$115
24-inch gate extension	$35

Collars	Plain	With name
Small	$4	$17
Medium	$6	$18
Large	$7	$20

1. Mrs. Garcia buys 2 flexible gates and 1 extension on sale.
   How much does she spend?

   Estimate?
   Exact answer?

2. An animal shelter has a discount coupon for $193 off a large purchase
   at the dog supply store. The shelter buys 113 medium dog collars with
   names and uses the discount coupon. What will be the final price?

   Estimate?
   Exact answer?

3. Emma bought a flexible gate for a room that is 8 feet wide.
   The gate is too short for her space. How many inches short is it?
   There are 12 inches in 1 foot.

   Estimate?
   Exact answer?

L E A R N

Estimate to Predict and Verify (B)

Predict, Solve, and Verify Answers

Estimate to predict the answer. Then solve. Write the estimate and the exact answer.

1. The Arden family has 3 German shepherd dogs. Daisy weighs 88 pounds, Lucky weighs 106 pounds, and Otto weighs 93 pounds. How much do the 3 dogs weigh altogether?

2. A science magazine reported that a giant freshwater catfish can weigh 644 pounds. Ethan says that the largest fish he ever caught was 7 pounds. How many times heavier was the giant catfish?

3. Andy's Art Store has 321 tubes of oil paint. If 106 tubes cost $5 each and the rest cost $3 each, how much will the store take in by selling all of them?

4. Tia's grandmother lives 2,956 miles away. Tia has driven 2,458 miles so far. How much farther does Tia have to drive to get to her grandmother's house?

Choose the answer.

5. Abigail collects horse figures, horse key chains, and other horse items. She has 1,922 horse items in her collection. She decides to give away part of her collection. If she gives away 473 horse items, how many will Abigail still have?

Which estimate could you use to verify that 1,449 is a reasonable answer to this problem?

A. 2,200 − 400   B. 1,500 − 500

C. 2,000 − 500   D. 2,200 − 500

TRY IT

Use Simpler Problems to Solve Harder Ones

Use a Simpler Problem

Worked Examples

The way you go about solving a simple story problem can help you to solve one that is similar but more complex. Problem 2 of these Worked Examples is harder than Problem 1, but both problems ask a similar question and the 4-step plan and strategy for solving them is the same.

PROBLEM 1 Sofia is an arts and crafts counselor at a summer day camp. She has 448 loose crayons to sort into boxes with 8 crayons in each box. How many full boxes of crayons will she have?

SOLUTION

UNDERSTAND THE PROBLEM You need to separate 448 crayons into 8 equal groups.

DEVISE A PLAN To solve the problem, you can write a division number sentence: $448 \div 8 = ?$

CARRY OUT THE PLAN

$$
\begin{array}{r}
56 \\
8\overline{)448} \\
-400 \\
\hline
48 \\
-48 \\
\hline
0
\end{array}
$$

← Estimate how many groups of 8 are in 448. Since 50×8 is 400, place a 5 in the quotient above the tens place in the dividend.

← Then multiply 50×8 and write 400.

← Next subtract $448 - 400$ to get 48. $48 \div 8$ is 6.

← Place the 6 in the quotient above the ones place in the dividend.

└ Multiply 6×8 and write 48.

└ Subtract $48 - 48 = 0$. There is no remainder.

LOOK BACK Make sure you've answered the question that was asked. Since 56 is close to the estimate of 50, then the answer makes sense.

ANSWER Sofia will have 56 full boxes of crayons.

LEARN

PROBLEM 2 Sofia has 1,113 large beads to sort. She needs to place 21 beads in each container. How many containers will she need?

SOLUTION

UNDERSTAND THE PROBLEM You need to separate 1,113 beads into equal groups of 21.

DEVISE A PLAN Use the same strategy that you used for Problem 1. Write a division number sentence: $1,113 \div 21 = ?$

CARRY OUT THE PLAN

$$
\begin{array}{r}
53 \\
21 \overline{)\, 1,113} \\
-\ 1,050 \\
\hline
63 \\
-\ 63 \\
\hline
0
\end{array}
$$

Estimate how many groups of 21 are in 1,113. Since 50×20 is 1,000, place the 5 in the quotient above the tens place in the dividend.

Then multiply 50×21 and write 1,050.

Next subtract $1,113 - 1,050$ to get 63. Estimate. Since 20×3 is 60, place the 3 in the quotient above the ones place in the dividend.

Multiply 3×21 and write 63.

Subtract $63 - 63 = 0$. There is no remainder.

LOOK BACK Make sure you've answered the question that was asked. Since 53 is close to the estimate of 50, then the answer makes sense.

ANSWER Sofia will need 53 containers.

Solve Problem 1 and explain your strategy. Then look at Problem 2 and explain why you can solve it the same way as Problem 1, and solve.

1. Mrs. Lee wants to share 85 muffins equally among 5 people.

   How many muffins will each person get?

2. Mrs. Lee wants to share 2,067 muffins among 53 people.

   How many muffins will each person get?

Solve Problem 3 and explain your strategy. Then look at Problem 4 and explain why you can solve it the same way as Problem 3, and solve.

3. Luis needs to tile a lobby area 9 feet wide and 9 feet long with large square tiles that are 3 feet long and 3 feet wide.

   How many tiles will he need?

4. Luis needs to tile a space 10 feet wide and 20 feet long. The tiles are 2 feet wide and 4 feet long.

   How many tiles will he need?

LEARN

Use Simpler Problems to Solve Harder Ones
Simple and Complex Problems

Worked Examples

To solve a complex story problem, think of a similar, but simpler, problem that you know how to solve. Then apply the same strategy you used to solve the simpler problem.

PROBLEM A potter makes 156 mugs. She wants to pack 12 mugs in each box. How many boxes does she need?

SOLUTION

UNDERSTAND THE PROBLEM You need to find out how many groups of 12 mugs are in 156 mugs.

DEVISE A PLAN Rewrite the problem with simpler numbers. Replace 156 mugs with 18 mugs in the problem. Then replace 12 mugs per box with 3 mugs. How would you solve this simpler problem? A potter makes 18 mugs. She wants to pack 3 mugs in each box. How many boxes does she need?

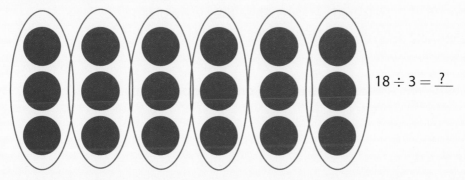

$$18 \div 3 = \underline{\ ?\ }$$

Use the diagram to sketch this simpler problem. Then write the number sentence that the diagram shows.

Now look at the original problem and write a number sentence similar to the one you wrote for the simpler problem. $156 \div 12 = ?$

Solve the number sentence.

L E A R N

CARRY OUT THE PLAN

$$\begin{array}{r} 13 \\ 12\overline{)156} \\ -120 \\ \hline 36 \\ -36 \\ \hline 0 \end{array}$$

← Estimate how many groups of 12 are in 156. Since 10×12 is 120, place a 1 in the quotient above the tens place in the dividend.

← Then multiply 10×12 and write 120.

← Next subtract $156 - 120$ to get 36. $36 \div 12$ is 3.

Place the 3 in the quotient above the ones place in the dividend.

Multiply 3×12 and write 36.

Subtract $36 - 36 = 0$. There is no remainder.

LOOK BACK Make sure you've answered the question that was asked. Since 13 is close to the estimate 10, the answer makes sense.

ANSWER The potter needs 13 boxes.

Read the problem. With simpler numbers, make a new problem and write a number sentence to solve. Then write a number sentence for the original problem and solve.

1. Members of the Enviro Club collected 2,272 cans. Then they were given 16 bags with 15 cans in each bag. How many cans do they have now?

    Make a simpler problem and write a number sentence.

    Members of the Enviro Club collected _?_ cans. Then they were given _?_ bags with _?_ cans in each bag. How many cans do they have now?

    _?_ + _?_ × _?_ = ?

    Solve the original problem. Remember to use the order of operations.

    2,272 ◯ 16 ◯ 15 = ?

    Answer: _?_ cans

2. A factory makes 2,272 cups. The cups will be packed into boxes with 16 cups in each box. How many boxes will the factory need?

    Make a simpler problem and write a number sentence.

    A factory makes _?_ cups. The cups will be packed into boxes with _?_ cups in each box. How many boxes will the factory need?

    _?_ ◯ _?_ = ?

    Solve the original problem.

    2,272 ◯ 16 = ?

    Answer: _?_ boxes

LEARN

3. The National Tower is 341 feet higher than the Central Tower.
The Northwestern Tower is 243 feet taller than the National Tower.
How much taller is the Northwestern Tower than the Central Tower?

Make a simpler problem and write a number sentence.

The National Tower is ⟶?⟵ feet higher than the Central Tower.
The Northwestern Tower is ⟶?⟵ feet taller than the National Tower.
How much taller is the Northwestern Tower than the Central Tower?

$\underline{\ ?\ } \bigcirc \underline{\ ?\ } = ?$

Solve the original problem.

$\underline{\ ?\ } \bigcirc \underline{\ ?\ } = ?$

Answer: ⟶?⟵ feet

Solve. Then explain how you used the sketches to solve the problem.

4. Mrs. Birch is planning a charity event. She makes sketches to show the number of
people who could sit at square tables pushed together into a rectangle.
She sketches 1, 2, 3, and 4 square tables pushed together.

| 4 people | 6 people | 8 people | 10 people |

How many people can sit at 8 tables pushed together?

Choose the answer.

5. Jacob looked at this number pattern.

7   14   21   28

He noticed the following pattern:

$7 \times 1 = 7$
$7 \times 2 = 14$
$7 \times 3 = 21$
$7 \times 4 = 28$

Jacob used this information to figure out other numbers in the pattern.
What is the 40th number in the pattern?

A. 56   B. 280   C. 350   D. 400

L E A R N

Represent and Explain Story Problems

More Than One Strategy to Solve

Worked Examples

You can use different strategies to solve a story problem. You can decide which strategy you want to use.

PROBLEM Johnny saw some animals at a pet store. He saw 4 cats. He saw 3 times as many dogs as cats. He saw 5 fewer hamsters than dogs. How many animals did Johnny see at the pet store?

SOLUTION 1

UNDERSTAND THE PROBLEM You need to find out how many cats Johnny saw, how many dogs he saw, and how many hamsters he saw at the pet store. Then you need to find out how many animals he saw in all.

DEVISE A PLAN You can draw a diagram. Use circles to show the different types of animals. Let C stand for cat, D for dog, and H for hamster.

- Johnny saw 4 cats. Draw 4 circles and write C in each circle.
- He saw 3 times as many dogs as cats. Draw 3 groups of 4 circles and write D in each circle.
- He saw 5 fewer hamsters than dogs. Count the number of D circles and draw 5 fewer circles. Write H in each circle.

CARRY OUT THE PLAN Use the diagram. Count the total number of circles. There are 23 circles, so Johnny saw 23 animals at the pet store.

C = cat

D = dog

H = hamster

LOOK BACK Be sure you answered the question. Reread the problem to be sure you drew the diagram correctly. Count the circles again.

ANSWER Johnny saw 23 animals at the pet store.

SOLUTION 2

UNDERSTAND THE PROBLEM See Solution 1.

DEVISE A PLAN This problem is a multistep problem. You need to break the problem into steps.

1. Remember that Johnny saw 4 cats.
2. Find the number of dogs Johnny saw.
3. Find the number of hamsters Johnny saw.
4. Write a number sentence to find the total number of animals Johnny saw. Then solve.

CARRY OUT THE PLAN

1. Johnny saw 4 cats.
2. He saw 3 times the number of dogs as cats. $3 \times 4 = ?$; $3 \times 4 = 12$ dogs
3. He saw 5 fewer hamsters than dogs. $12 - 5 = ?$; $12 - 5 = 7$ hamsters
4. $4 + 12 + 7 = ?$; $4 + 12 + 7 = 23$ animals

LOOK BACK Be sure you answered the question. Reread the problem step-by-step to be sure you computed each part correctly.

ANSWER Johnny saw 23 animals at the pet store.

Explain how to solve the story problem two different ways. Then solve.

1. Kerry invited 16 people to her birthday party. 6 people can sit at a long dining-room table. 4 people can sit at a square table. What is the fewest number of square tables needed so each guest will have a seat?

2. A recipe calls for 0.35 ounces of sprinkles on each dozen cookies. Lyle wants to decorate 36 cookies. How many ounces of sprinkles will Lyle need?

3. A statue of a man is 12.7 feet tall. The base that it sits on is 5.4 feet high. It traveled 345 miles to be put in place. How tall is the statue from the bottom of the base to the top of the statue's head?

Represent and Explain Story Problems

Same Problem, Different Ways

Worked Examples

You can make a table or draw a diagram to solve a story problem.

PROBLEM Sarah has two dogs. Prince eats 2 cans of dog food every 3 days and 1 bag of dry food in 12 days. Bucky eats 2 cans of dog food every 2 days and 2 bags of dry food in 12 days. For how many days can Sarah feed both dogs with 40 cans of dog food and 6 bags of dry food?

SOLUTION 1

UNDERSTAND THE PROBLEM You need to find the number of days Sarah can feed her two dogs with the food that she has.

DEVISE A PLAN Use the make-a-table strategy.

1 Make one table to figure out how many cans Prince eats in 12 days.

2 Make another table to figure out how many cans Bucky eats in 12 days.

3 Compare the total amount of food the dogs eat in 12 days to the total amount of food that Sarah has. Then decide how many days the food will last.

CARRY OUT THE PLAN

1

Prince's Food				
Days	3	6	9	12
Cans	2	4	6	8

Prince eats 8 cans and 1 bag of food in 12 days.

2

Bucky's Food						
Days	2	4	6	8	10	12
Cans	2	4	6	8	10	12

Bucky eats 12 cans and 2 bags of food in 12 days.

LEARN

3 They eat $8 + 12 = 20$ cans of food and $1 + 2 = 3$ bags of food in 12 days. Since 40 cans of food $= 2 \times 20$ cans and 6 bags of food $= 2 \times 3$ bags, then Sarah will have enough food for 2×12 days $= 24$ days.

LOOK BACK Does 24 days answer the question? Yes, because you need to find for how many days Sarah can feed her dog with 40 cans and 6 bags. That's exactly how much food the dogs will eat in 24 days.

SOLUTION 2

UNDERSTAND THE PROBLEM See Solution 1.

DEVISE A PLAN Use the draw-a-diagram strategy.

1 Draw a diagram to find how many cans of food the dogs eat in 12 days.

2 Draw another diagram to find how many bags of food the dogs eat in 12 days.

3 Compare the total amount of food the dogs eat in 12 days to the total amount of food that Sarah has.

CARRY OUT THE PLAN

1 Cans
Days

Prince

Cans
Days

Bucky

Sarah needs $8 + 12 = 20$ cans in 12 days.

cans

2 Bags
Days

Prince

Bags
Days

Bucky

Sarah needs $1 + 2 = 3$ bags in 12 days.

3 So they will eat $2 \times 20 = 40$ cans of food and $2 \times 3 = 6$ bags of food in 2×12, or 24 days.

LOOK BACK See Solution 1.

ANSWER With the food she has, Sarah can feed her dogs for 24 days.

L E A R N

Solve the problem two different ways.

1. Alex has $1.40 in his pocket. He has 11 coins in all. He has 3 quarters and a combination of dimes and nickels.

   How many dimes does Alex have?

   How many nickels does Alex have?

2. A novelty store has 350 toy figures of popular music stars. Each bin holds 25 figures.

   How many bins will hold all 350 figures?

3. The Antonini family bought hot dog rolls in packages of 10 and hot dogs in packages of 6. Each adult at the picnic eats 3 hot dogs and 3 hot dog rolls.

   How many packages of rolls and hot dogs will the family have to buy to feed 20 adults?

Represent and Explain Story Problems

Identify Two Strategies

Solve two ways. Explain the strategies.

1. Bryson bought some pencils, pens, and markers at the office supply store. He bought 3 times as many pencils as pens. He bought 5 more markers than pens. He bought 6 pens. How many items did Bryson buy at the office supply store?

Choose the two strategies that can be used to solve the problem.

2. Anna had some flowers. She arranged 18 flowers in each of 8 vases. She had 11 flowers left over. How many flowers did she have to start?

   A. Guess and test. Try starting with 100 flowers. Subtract 21 repeatedly until the difference is less than 21. Count the number of times you subtracted. If you did not subtract 21 eight times and end up with 11 flowers left over, 100 is not right. Adjust the number and repeat.

   B. Write a number sentence and solve.
   $8 \times 18 + 11 = \underline{\ ?\ }$

   C. Draw a picture. Sketch 8 groups of 18, then 11 more, and count them all.

3. Volunteers are setting up benches for an exhibition at a town fair. They will use long benches that can seat 12 people each and short benches that can seat 5 people each. What is the fewest number of short benches that volunteers can set up so that 58 people can have seats?

   A. Draw a picture. Draw 58 dots. Circle as many groups of 12 as you can. Then circle as many groups of 5 as you can from the dots that are not already circled. Count the number of groups of 5.

   B. Work backward. Begin with 58. Subtract 12 repeatedly until the difference is less than 12. Then subtract 5 until the difference is less than 5. Count the number of 5s you subtracted.

   C. Write number sentences and solve.
   $5 \times 12 = 60$ and $60 - 58 = \underline{\ ?\ }$

   D. Explain that 5 times 10 equals 50, so you need 10 short benches.

4. A frozen yogurt shop owner sold vanilla, chocolate, and banana yogurt pops. In one hour, the owner sold one more banana pop than chocolate pops. She sold twice as many vanilla pops as banana pops. If the owner sold 7 chocolate pops, how many total pops did she sell in one hour?

A. Work backward. She sold 7 chocolate pops, so multiply 7 by 2 and add 1.

B. Draw a diagram. Draw 7 chocolate pops. Then draw 1 more banana pop than chocolate pops, or 8 banana pops. Then draw two times as many vanilla pops as banana pops, or 16 vanilla pops. Count all the yogurt pops to find the total.

C. Use logical thinking. There were 7 chocolate pops. Add 1 to get 8 because one more banana than chocolate pops was sold. Double the 8 to get 16 because twice as many vanilla as banana pops were sold. Then add $7 + 8 + 16$.

D. Write a number sentence and solve.
$2 \times 7 + 1 = \underline{\ ?\ }$

TRY IT

State Solutions Clearly (A)
Make–a–Table Strategy

Worked Examples

You can make a table to organize the data in a story problem.

PROBLEM Layla recorded the daily high and low temperatures in her city for five days: Highs: Mon. 81°, Tues. 82°, Wed. 80°, Thurs. 80°, Fri. 79°; Lows: Mon. 63°, Tues. 65°, Wed. 60°, Thurs. 67°, Fri. 62°. On which day was the difference between the high and low temperatures the greatest? Solve and explain how you solved the problem.

SOLUTION

UNDERSTAND THE PROBLEM To see which day of the week had the greatest difference in temperatures, find the difference between the high and low temperatures of each day.

DEVISE A PLAN Use the make-a-table strategy. Arrange the data by days of the week so that the lows can easily be subtracted from the highs. Subtract. Identify the day with the greatest difference. Then explain how you solved the problem.

CARRY OUT THE PLAN

	Mon.	Tues.	Wed.	Thurs.	Fri.
High Temp.	81°	82°	80°	80°	79°
Low Temp.	63°	65°	60°	67°	62°
Difference	18°	17°	20°	13°	17°

The greatest difference was 20° and occurred on Wednesday.

LOOK BACK Be sure the data on the table matches the data in the problem. Check your subtraction and compare the differences again.

ANSWER The greatest difference occurred on Wednesday. To solve the problem, subtract each day's low temperature from its high temperature, find the greatest difference, and identify the day it occurred.

L E A R N

Complete the table to solve the problem.

1. The city of Twin Lakes has a weeklong town carnival each year. Mr. Buckle recorded the number of adult tickets and child tickets that were sold each day.

Adult tickets:
Monday 318
Tuesday 425
Wednesday 376
Thursday 404
Friday 418
Saturday 514
Sunday 511

Child tickets:
Monday 375
Tuesday 350
Wednesday 480
Thursday 270
Friday 500
Saturday 320
Sunday 285

On which day did the carnival sell the most tickets?

How many more tickets were sold on Wednesday than on Tuesday?

Explain how you solved the problem.

	Monday	Tuesday	Wednesday	Thursday	Friday	Saturday	Sunday
Adult tickets	?	?	?	?	?	?	?
Child tickets	?	?	?	?	?	?	?
Total	?	?	?	?	?	?	?

2. Ashley has 1 dime, 5 nickels, and 20 pennies. She found six ways to use some of her coins to show 18¢. Use the table to find the six ways that Ashley can use some of her coins to show 18¢.

Then explain how you solved the problem.

Number of Dimes	Number of Nickels	Number of Pennies	Total Value
?	?	?	18¢
?	?	?	18¢
?	?	?	18¢
?	?	?	18¢
?	?	?	18¢
?	?	?	18¢

LEARN

Read the problem and follow the directions.

3. Write a story problem that uses the data in the table. Then solve the problem and explain how you solved it.

	Art Club	Music Club	Dance Club	Sport Club	Chess Club
Money raised	$675	$715	$682	$764	$520
Expenses	$411	$430	$459	$582	$322
?	?	?	?	?	?

LEARN

State Solutions Clearly (A)

Solve and Explain

Explain how to solve the problem, and then solve.

1. Tickets for the zoo cost $15 each for adult tickets and $9 each for child tickets. Mrs. Porter bought 8 tickets. She spent a total of $90. How many of each type of ticket did Mrs. Porter buy?

2. Zeke is saving money to buy a new bike. The bike costs $218. He starts with $42 in his savings account. Each week he deposits $15. How many weeks will it take for Zeke to save enough to buy the bike?

Choose the explanation that best describes how to solve the problem.

3. Elena ran 20 miles every week for 5 weeks. She ran 25 miles the sixth week and 33 miles the seventh week. How far did Elena run in 7 weeks?

    A. **Write a number sentence.** $20 + 5 + 25 + 6 + 33 + 7 = \underline{\ ?\ }$
        Elena ran 96 miles.

    B. **Break up the problem into smaller problems.** Multiply 20 by 5 to get 100 miles in 5 weeks. Add 25 miles and 33 miles to figure out how many miles she ran in the sixth and seventh weeks. Add $100 + 58$ together. Elena ran 158 miles.

    C. **Work backward.** Elena ran 20 miles in 5 weeks. That means she ran 4 miles in 1 week. Add 4 miles to 25 and 33. Elena ran 62 miles.

    D. **Make a table.** Elena ran 33 miles.

Week	1	2	3	4	5	6	7
Miles	20	20	20	20	20	25	33

TRY IT

4. The zoo has 32 lizards in the enclosure. 10 of the lizards are yellow, and 6 of the lizards are red. Half of the remaining lizards are green. How many lizards are green?

    A. **Work backward.** Start with the original number of lizards. Divide by 2 as half of the lizards are green, and then subtract 10 and 6.

    B. **Guess and test.** Guess that there are 10 green lizards. Half of 10 is 5. Add 10 and add 6 to get 21. That is fewer than the number of lizards in the zoo, so try again with another number. Guess that there are 40 green lizards. Half of 40 is 20. Add 10 and add 6 to get 36. That is more than the number of lizards in the zoo, so try again with another number. Guess that there are 32 green lizards. Half of 32 is 16. Add 10 and add 6 to get 32.

    C. **Write a number sentence.** $(32 - 10 - 6) \times 2 = \underline{\ ?\ }$

    D. **Make a diagram.** Draw 32 dots to represent the 32 lizards. Cross out 10 of them for the yellow lizards and 6 of them for the red lizards. Take the remaining 16 dots and cross out half of them (8 dots). The number of dots remaining is the number of green lizards in the zoo.

5. Carl spent 45 minutes on his French homework, and 1 hour on his math homework. He talked on the phone for 15 minutes and then drove to his tennis practice. The drive took 20 minutes. His tennis practice started at 5:30 p.m. What time did Carl start his French homework?

    A. **Guess and test.** Start at 2:00, and add 45 minutes. The time is now 2:45. Add 1 hour. The time is now 3:45. Add 15 minutes. The time is now 4:00. Add 20 minutes. Carl started his French homework at 4:20.

    B. **Write a number sentence.** $530 - (45 + 1 + 15 + 20) = \underline{\ ?\ }$
       Carl started his French homework at 4:49.

    C. **Make a diagram.** Draw a clock. First show the minute hand starting at 12. Draw another clock. Add 45 minutes. The minute hand now points to the 9. Draw another clock. Add 1 hour. The minute hand points to the 9. Draw another clock. Add 15 minutes. The minute hand now points to the 12. Draw another clock. Add 20 minutes. The minute hand now points to the 5. Carl started his French homework at 25 minutes after the hour.

    D. **Work backward.** Start at 5:30, and subtract 20 minutes; he left for tennis practice at 5:10. Subtract 15 minutes; he started talking on the phone at 4:55. Subtract 1 hour; he started math homework at 3:55. Subtract 45 minutes. Carl started his French homework at 3:10.

TRY IT

6. Susie bought a balloon and a card to give to her grandfather every month. Each balloon cost $7 and each card cost $2. How much money did Susie spend in 6 months?

   A. **Make a table.** Susie spent $54.

Month	1	2	3	4	5	6
Total Cost	$9	$18	$27	$36	$45	$54

   B. **Draw a picture.** Draw 7 circles and write $7 in each one. Draw 2 circles and write $2 in each one. Add up the amounts in the circles. Susie spent $53.

   C. **Use objects to model the problem.** Take 7 blocks and 2 blocks and put them together to get 9 blocks. Susie spent $9 altogether.

   D. **Break the problem into steps.** Multiply the cost of flowers by the cost of the card ($7 × $2). Multiply the cost by the number of months ($14 × $6). Susie spent $84.

7. Rachael rode her bike 15 miles every week for 5 weeks. She rode her bike 18 miles the sixth week and 19 miles the seventh week. How far did Rachael ride her bike in 7 weeks?

   A. Add 15 and 5 and 18 and 6 and 19 and 7.

   B. Add 15 and 5. Then add 18 and 19. Then add the two sums together.

   C. Multiply 15 × 5. Then add 18 and 19 to the product.

   D. Divide 15 by 5. Then add 18 and 19 to the quotient.

8. Six boys want to go to the movies and then go for pizza. They have a total of $100. The movie tickets cost $10 each. How much money will the boys have left to buy pizza?

   A. Add 6 and 100 and 10.

   B. Divide 100 by 6. Then add 10 to the quotient.

   C. Multiply 10 × 6. Then subtract the product from 100.

   D. Add 10 and 6. Then multiply the sum by 100.

9. Over summer vacation, Alice read 3 books a week for the first 3 weeks and then 2 books a week for the last 3 weeks. How many books did Alice read?

   A. Add 3 and 3 and 2 and 3.

   B. Add 3 and 2. Multiply the sum by 2.

   C. Multiply 3 × 3. Then multiply 2 × 3. Then add the two products.

   D. Add 3 and 3. Then divide the sum by 3.

TRY IT

10. The toy factory makes 120 toy cars in a day. Each day 10 of the cars are rejected because they have flaws in the paint. How many flawless cars can the toy factory make in 400 days?

   A. Add 120 and 10 and 400.

   B. Multiply 120 × 10. Subtract the product from 400.

   C. Divide 120 by 10. Add the quotient to 400.

   D. Subtract 10 from 120. Multiply the difference by 400.

Choose the explanation that best describes the answer to the problem.

11. A sports club can have a maximum of 15 people in each yoga class. How many classes will the club need if 87 people sign up for yoga?

   A. Divide 87 by 15. The answer is 5 with 12 left over. So the club will need 5 classes.

   B. Multiply 87 by 15. The answer is 1,218. So the club will need 1,218 classes.

   C. Divide 87 by 15. The answer is 5 with 12 left over. So the club will need 6 classes.

   D. Multiply 87 by 15. The answer is 1,305. So the club will need 1,305 classes.

12. The farmworkers put 12 eggs in each box. They boxed 3,364 eggs in one month. How many complete boxes did the workers fill?

   A. Divide 3,364 by 12. The answer is 280 with 4 left over. So the farmworkers can fill 281 boxes.

   B. Divide 3,364 by 12. The answer is 280 with 4 left over. So the farmworkers can fill 280 boxes.

   C. Divide 3,364 by 12. The answer is 28 with 4 left over. So the farmworkers can fill 29 boxes.

   D. Divide 3,364 by 12. The answer is 276 with 5 left over. So the farmworkers can fill 277 boxes.

T R Y   I T

State Solutions Clearly (B)

Work-Backward Strategy

Worked Examples

You can use the work-backward strategy to solve a story problem.

PROBLEM Layla has an eye appointment at 9:30 a.m. tomorrow. She needs to be there 15 minutes early to fill out forms. It takes her 30 minutes to get ready in the morning and she needs to allow 25 minutes to get to the eye doctor's office from home. At what time should Layla start getting ready tomorrow?

Solve. Then explain how you solved the problem

SOLUTION

UNDERSTAND THE PROBLEM The ending time is given (9:30 a.m.) and the starting time needs to be found. (The starting time is when Layla needs to start getting ready.)

DEVISE A PLAN Work backward. Start at the time Layla must be at the doctor's office. Then move back the number of minutes it takes each event to happen to find what time she should start getting ready.

CARRY OUT THE PLAN Start at the ending time and move back by subtracting the minutes Layla will spend on each event.

start here
↓

8:20 a.m. ← minus 30 min ← 8:50 a.m. ← minus 25 min ← 9:15 a.m. ← minus 15 min ← 9:30 a.m.

So 8:20 a.m. is the time Layla should start getting ready.

LOOK BACK To be sure the answer makes sense, write the answer, 8:20 a.m., on the far left. Add the minutes for each event, moving to the right. Since the result is 9:30 a.m., then the answer of 8:20 a.m. is correct.

8:20 a.m. → plus 30 min → 8:50 a.m. → plus 25 min → 9:15 a.m. → plus 15 min → 9:30 a.m.

ANSWER Layla should start getting ready at 8:20 a.m. To solve the problem, you start at the ending time. You subtract the minutes Layla spent on each event, recording the time before each event. The final time you record is the time Layla should start getting ready.

LEARN

Solve. Then explain how you solved the problem.

1. Carl started with some money in his savings account. He withdrew $30, then deposited $75. Next he deposited $40 and withdrew $50. Now he has $148. How much money did Carl start with in his savings account?

2. Some people were at the museum when it opened at 10:00 a.m. By noon, 98 people had entered the museum and 32 people had left. From noon until 8:00 p.m., 128 more people arrived and 79 left. At 8:00 p.m., 200 people remained in the museum. How many people were at the museum when it opened?

Read the problem and follow the directions.

3. Write a 3- or 4-sentence story problem that uses the information in the table. Then work backward to solve the problem.

Movie title	Start time	Length of movie
Shark Attack!	1:30 p.m., 4:30 p.m., 7:00 p.m.	109 minutes
Friends in Space	1:15 p.m., 3:50 p.m., 6:30 p.m.	117 minutes
Playground Capers	1:25 p.m., 4:45 p.m., 7:15 p.m.	110 minutes
Mystery Mission	1:20 p.m., 4:15 p.m., 6:45 p.m.	98 minutes

LEARN

Problem-Solving Strategies

Select the Strategy

Worked Examples

For each story problem, some problem-solving strategies are more helpful than others. Before you devise a plan, you need to look for strategies that will help you correctly solve the problem. You also need to identify strategies that will not help you correctly solve the problem.

PROBLEM Which strategy would **not** correctly solve this story problem?

Trent wants to get a cell phone. The phone costs $50. Cell phone service costs $42 a month. How much money does Trent need to get a cell phone and service for 6 months?

A. Make a table.

Month	1	2	3	4	5	6
Total Cost	$92	$134	$176	$218	$260	?

B. Make a line graph.

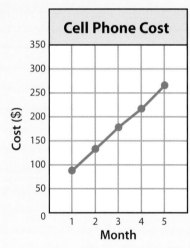

C. Write a number sentence. $\longrightarrow$ $50 + (42 \times 6) = \underline{\ ?\ }$

D. Make a model. $\longrightarrow$ Take 42 pieces of play money.
Divide the money into 6 equal groups.
Add $50 to each group.

SOLUTION

UNDERSTAND THE PROBLEM You need to find out which strategy would **not** correctly solve this story problem.

DEVISE A PLAN Look at each answer choice and ask yourself, "Will this strategy correctly solve this story problem? Why or why not?" The answer choice that will **not** correctly solve this story problem is the correct answer.

CARRY OUT THE PLAN

- **Answer choice A.** Yes. The table shows the amount Trent would spend each month and includes the cost of the phone and the monthly service fee. If you complete the table, you will find the amount spent in 6 months.

- **Answer choice B.** Yes. The graph shows a linear relationship because the same amount, or $42, is spent each month after the first month. If you extend the straight line with a straightedge, you will find the amount that will be spent in 6 months.

- **Answer choice C.** Yes. The monthly fee is $42, so the monthly fee for 6 months is $42 × 6. Add this to the cost of the cell phone ($50) to get the equation $50 + (42 \times 6) = \underline{\ ?\ }$. If you solve this number sentence, you will find the amount that will be spent in 6 months.

- **Answer choice D.** No. This model shows division instead of multiplication. It would **not** correctly solve this problem, so it is the correct answer choice.

LOOK BACK Make sure you've answered the question that was asked. Have you found the answer choice that will **not** correctly solve this story problem?

ANSWER Answer choice D is the correct answer to the question, "Which strategy does **not** correctly solve this story problem?"

Choose the strategy that would **not** correctly solve the problem.

1. Samantha notices that it is 2:15 p.m. now. Her friend Shelly called her 30 minutes ago. At that time, Shelly told Samantha that she had left home in another city 2 hours and 45 minutes earlier to come visit. What time did Shelly leave home?

   A. **Work backward.** The end time is 2:15 p.m. Subtract (go back) 30 minutes. Then subtract (go back) 2 hours and 45 minutes to find the start time.

   B. **Look for a pattern.**
      2 hours 15 minutes
      0 minutes
      2 hours 45 minutes

   C. **Guess and test.** Guess a time before 2:15 and then check if it works with the information in the problem. Add 2 hours 45 minutes to the time and then add another 30 minutes. If the end time is 2:15 p.m., the start time is correct.

   D. **Make a model.** Use or draw a clock to model the problem. Set the time to 2:15. Then move the minute hand back half a turn to show 30 minutes. This is the time of the phone call. Then move the minute hand back again to show 45 minutes. Move the hour hand back 2 numbers to show the 2 hours. The time shown is the start time.

LEARN

Choose the strategy that would not correctly solve the problem.

2. Helen had some pocket money. Her sister had $6 and Helen had twice as much money as her sister. Helen spent $2 at the post office and $3 at the newspaper store. How much money did Helen have left?

   A. **Use objects to model the problem.** Take 6 pieces of play money. Take away 2 pieces and then take away 3 pieces.

   B. **Draw a diagram.** Draw 6 dots to represent how much money Helen's sister has. Draw 12 dots to show how much money Helen has. Cross out 2 of Helen's dots to represent the money she spent at the post office. Cross out 3 of Helen's dots to represent the money she spent at the newspaper store. Circle the remaining dots in Helen's group.

   C. **Use logical reasoning.** Multiply 6 by 2 to figure out how much money Helen has to begin with. The answer is 12. Subtract 2 from 12 for the money Helen spent at the post office. The answer is 10. Subtract 3 from 10 for the money Helen spent at the newspaper store.

   D. **Translate into a number sentence.** $(6 \times 2) - (3 + 2) = \underline{\ ?\ }$

Choose the strategy that would correctly solve the story problem.

3. A square game board has 4 small squares in each row and 4 small squares in each column. How would you shade the small squares so that each row and each column has 2 and only 2 small squares shaded?

   A. **Use logical reasoning.** If the square game board has 4 squares in each row and column, then to have 2 squares shaded in each row and column, shade 1 square in each row and 1 square in each column.

   B. **Draw a diagram.** On grid paper, draw a square that is 4 squares wide and 4 squares long. Shade 2 squares in each row. Check if the diagram shows 2 and only 2 small squares shaded in each column. Repeat if it does not. Continue until you find a combination that matches the information in the problem.

   C. **Write a number sentence.** $(4 \times 4) \div 2 = \underline{\ ?\ }$

Choose the strategy that would **not** correctly solve the problem.

1. Susie bought a sandwich and an iced tea each day at work. Each sandwich cost $4 and each iced tea cost $2. How much money did Susie spend in 7 days?

   A. **Write a number sentence.**
      $(7 \times 4) + (7 \times 2) = \underline{?}$

   B. **Make a coordinate graph.**

   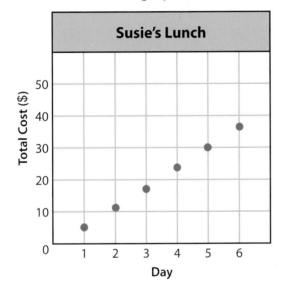

   C. **Make a table.**

   Susie's Lunch

Day	1	2	3	4	5	6	7
Total Cost ($)	$6	$12	$18	$24	$30	$36	?

   D. **Use objects to model the problem.** Take 4 pieces of play money. Divide the money into 2 equal groups. Add $7 to each group.

TRY IT

2. There are 21 children at the summer camp. There are 2 times as many boys as girls. How many boys are there at the summer camp?

   A. **Draw a diagram.** Draw 21 dots. Divide the group into 3 equal groups. Draw a rectangle around 2 of the groups. Count the number of dots inside the rectangle.

   B. **Use logical reasoning.** To find out how many children at the summer camp are boys, divide the total number into 3 groups, which gives 7 in each group. As there are twice as many boys as girls, multiply 7 by 2 to get 14.

   C. **Write a number sentence.**
   $(21 \div 3) \times 2 = \underline{?}$

   D. **Work backward.** There are 21 children at the camp. There are twice as many boys as girls, so divide by 2 to find out how many boys are at the summer camp.

3. Annie made $460 one summer. She spent $40 on some camping equipment, she spent twice as much on a new bicycle, and she spent half of what was left on her vacation. How much money did Annie spend on her vacation?

   A. **Use logical reasoning.** Start with $460. Subtract $40 to get $420. Multiply $40 by 2 to get the amount spent on the bicycle. Subtract $80 from $420 to get $340. Divide $340 by 2 to get the amount Annie spent on her vacation.

   B. **Draw a diagram.** Draw 46 tallies, one for each $10 Annie earned. Cross out 4 tallies for the $40 she spent on camping equipment. Cross out 8 tallies for the $80 spent on the bicycle. Circle half of the remaining tallies and multiply the number by $10.

   C. **Write a number sentence.**
   $\$460 - (\$40 + \$40 \times 2) = \$340$
   $\$340 \div 2 = \underline{?}$

   D. **Guess and test.** Guess that Annie spent $100 on her vacation. Add $40 + $80 to $100 to get $220. Then multiply by 2.

4. Victor is raising money for charity. He raises $4 for each mile he runs and $2 for each mile he rides his bike. How much money will Victor raise if he runs for 5 miles and rides his bike for 10 miles?

   A. **Use logical reasoning.**
      Step 1: Multiply $4 by 5 to figure out how much money Victor makes from running.
      Step 2: Then multiply $2 by 10 to figure out how much money Victor makes from riding his bike.
      Step 3: Add the two products together.

   B. **Write a number sentence.**
      $(4 \times 5) + (2 \times 10) = \underline{\ ?\ }$

   C. **Use objects to model the problem.** Use play money.
      Make 5 groups of $4. Make 10 groups of $2. Add up the money.

   D. **Draw a diagram.** Draw 2 circles. In one write $4 and in the other write $2. Draw a large circle around both of them to show how much money Victor makes.

5. Kelly invited 120 people to the wedding. 30 of them were her family members. 25 of them were her husband's family members, and the rest were friends of the family. How many friends of the family were invited to the wedding?

   A. **Write a number sentence.**
      $120 - (30 + 25) = \underline{\ ?\ }$

   B. **Use logical reasoning.** Add together the number of Kelly's family (30) and the number of her husband's family (25) to find the total number of family members. Subtract this from 120 (the number of people invited) to find the number of family friends invited.

   C. **Work backward.** Start with 120. Subtract 30 (the number of people from Kelly's family). Then subtract 25 (the number of people from her husband's family). The number left is the number of family friends who were invited.

   D. **Draw a diagram.** Draw 12 tallies, each one representing 10 guests. Cross out 3 tallies and then cross out 2 tallies. Multiply the number of tallies left by 10.

6. Charlotte had some pineapples to sell at the fruit stand. Her friend gave her another 4 pineapples to sell. Charlotte sold 12 pineapples. Charlotte has 10 pineapples left over. How many pineapples did Charlotte have to begin with?

A. **Draw a diagram.** Draw 10 pineapples. Draw 12 pineapples for the pineapples that were sold, and cross out 4 pineapples for the ones Charlotte's friend gave her. Count how many are left over to find the number Charlotte had to begin with.

B. **Work backward.** Start with the number of pineapples that Charlotte has left (10). Add the pineapples that were sold (12) and take away the pineapples that Charlotte's friend gave her (4).

C. **Use logical reasoning.** Charlotte had 10 pineapples left. Her friend gave her 4, so add 4. She sold 12, so subtract 12.

D. **Write a number sentence.**
$10 + 12 - 4 = \underline{\ ?\ }$

Estimated and Exact Answers

Determine Accuracy and Solve

Worked Examples

Before you solve a story problem, it's helpful to decide whether the answer should be exact or approximate.

PROBLEM A website for children receives an average of 985 visits per hour from 8 a.m. to 8 p.m. On any given day, how many visits will the website likely receive between 8 a.m. and 8 p.m.?

Does the problem need an approximate or exact answer? Why?
What is the answer?

SOLUTION

UNDERSTAND THE PROBLEM The question asks how many visits the website will *likely* receive between 8 a.m. and 8 p.m. The word *likely* tells you that you can estimate, or find an approximate answer.

DEVISE A PLAN To solve, round 985 to the nearest thousand. Then multiply the rounded number by 12, the number of hours between 8 a.m. and 8 p.m.

CARRY OUT THE PLAN 985 rounded to the nearest thousand is 1,000.
$1,000 \times 12 = 12,000$

LOOK BACK The answer 12,000 makes sense because the website receives almost 1,000 visits each hour over 12 hours.

ANSWER The problem needs an approximate answer because the question asks how many visits the website will *likely* receive. The website will likely receive about 12,000 visits between 8 a.m. and 8 p.m.

L E A R N

Read the problem and answer the questions.

1. In a balloon toss game, each team had 3 pairs of players. The judges added the longest distance that each pair of players tossed a balloon without breaking it. Look at the distances for each team in the chart. Which team had the highest sum of distances and won the balloon toss game?

   Does the problem need an approximate or exact answer? Why? What is the answer?

Maximum Distance (in feet)		
	Red Team	Blue Team
Pair 1	10.29	13.48
Pair 2	13.05	8.12
Pair 3	11.33	10.91

2. Hannah polled her friends to see how many minutes they listen to music each day. Then she made a table showing the results. She wanted to know how many of her friends listen to music for at least 90 minutes every day. So she analyzed the results to find the answer: 54 friends listen to music for 90 minutes or more each day.

Number of minutes	Less than 30	30 to 59	60 to 89	90 to 119	120 to 149	150 to 179	180 or more
Number of friends	15	27	29	21	18	12	3

   Is Hannah's answer an exact or approximate number?
   What did Hannah find out?

3. Josh wants to build a wooden bench that is 20.5 feet long. He has 3 lengths of board: 4.83 feet, 7.62 feet, and 9.87 feet. Does he have enough board to build the bench?

   Should Josh find an approximate or an exact answer? Why or why not? What is the answer?

LEARN

Estimated and Exact Answers

Explain Accuracy and Solve

Read the problem and follow the directions.

1. The National Park Service reported that 273,488,751 people visited U.S. national parks in a recent year. It is expected that an additional 100,000 will visit the parks next year. About how many people will visit the parks next year? (Express your answer to the nearest hundred thousand.)

2. Joan is at a restaurant and wants to order soup, a sandwich, and a glass of milk. She is trying to decide if she has enough money to order a cup of soup or a bowl of soup. A cup of soup costs $2.99 and a bowl of soup costs $4.49. A sandwich costs $4.95 and a glass of milk costs $1.98. Joan has $10.00.

   Explain one reason why Joan would want to simply estimate the cost of her meal.

   Explain one reason why Joan would want to figure out the exact cost of the meal.

Choose the answer.

3. Tony wants to buy some acrylic paint. He needs 40 mL of bright red, 65 mL of cobalt blue, and 50 mL of olive green. Each bottle holds 59 mL of paint.

   Which statement is correct?

   A. Tony should add all the amounts together and buy exactly 155 mL of paint, or 2.6 bottles of paint.

   B. Tony must calculate each amount separately and buy 1 bottle of bright red paint, 2 bottles of cobalt blue paint, and 1 bottle of olive green paint.

   C. Tony can round each number to the nearest 50 and add to find that he needs 150 mL of paint, or 2.5 bottles.

4. Sammie wants to buy a tube of gold oil paint that costs $8.79, a tube of bright red that costs $6.59, and a large tube of zinc white that costs $21.61. Sammie has $38.00.

Which **two** statements are correct?

A. If Sammie rounds the costs to the nearest dollar, she will know whether the cashier has given her the correct amount of change.

B. If Sammie rounds the costs to the nearest dollar, she can estimate whether she has enough money to buy the paint.

C. If Sammie calculates exactly how much the paint costs, she will know whether the cashier is charging her the correct amount of money.

5. A plumber is installing a bathroom. The plans call for seven pieces of pipe to be cut 4.6 in. long and three pieces of pipe to be cut 5.1 in. long.

Which statement is correct?

A. The plumber can cut 10 pieces of pipe exactly 5 in. long.

B. The plumber should cut the pieces to the exact measurements given.

C. The plumber can cut each piece of pipe about 5 in. long.

6. Janie is making strawberry pies. She needs 5 cups of strawberries for each pie.

Which statement is correct?

A. It is impossible to measure exactly 5 cups of strawberries, so Janie should put the strawberries in the blender and then measure 5 cups.

B. Janie should cut the strawberries into very tiny pieces so that she can use exactly 5 cups of strawberries.

C. Janie can use approximately 5 cups of strawberries for each pie.

7. A sandwich costs $5.95 and a glass of milk costs $1.25. The cashier is calculating the bill.

Which statement is correct?

A. The cashier must add the exact amounts.

B. The cashier can round the prices before adding.

TRY IT

8. Roberto wants to buy a T-shirt that costs $8.99, a pair of sandals that cost $4.79, and a baseball cap that costs $5.98. Roberto has $20.00 to spend.

Which **two** statements are true?

A. If Roberto calculates exactly how much he will spend, he will know that the cashier is charging him the correct amount of money.

B. If Roberto estimates the total cost by adding $9 + 5 + 6$, he will know that he has enough money to buy the three things.

C. If Roberto rounds the amounts and adds $9 + 5 + 6$, he will be able to check to make sure the cashier gave him the correct change.

9. The American marathon runner ran 5,824 miles in one year. The Swedish marathon runner ran 4,954 miles in one year. About how many miles did the two runners run altogether? (Give the answer to the nearest hundred.)

A. 10,700 miles   B. 10,800 miles   C. 10,900 miles   D. 11,000 miles

10. The observation deck on the Empire State Building is 1,211 feet from the ground. The observation deck on the Eiffel Tower is 902 feet from the ground. About how much higher is the deck on the Empire State Building than the Eiffel Tower? (Give the answer to the nearest ten.)

A. 300 feet   B. 310 feet   C. 320 feet   D. 400 feet

11. Martin traveled 1,985 miles each business trip. He took 12 business trips in one year. About how far did Martin travel for business trips in one year? (Give the answer to the nearest thousand.)

A. 2,000 miles   B. 12,000 miles   C. 20,000 miles   D. 24,000 miles

12. Frank needed to drive 2,420 miles. He wanted to drive the distance in 6 days, and he wanted to drive the same distance each day. About how far will he drive each day? (Give the answer to the nearest hundred.)

A. 14,400 miles   B. 4,000 miles   C. 500 miles   D. 400 miles

13. The cafeteria bought 32 pounds of cheese for $116. About how much did 1 pound of cheese cost? (Give the answer to the nearest dollar.)

A. $2   B. $3   C. $4   D. $5

TRY IT

Define and Sketch Triangles

Classify Triangles

Solve.

1. What is the name of a triangle that has only 2 of its 3 sides the same length?

   i DO NOt know?

2. How is an acute triangle different from both an obtuse triangle and a right triangle?

   one is small one is big and one is right

Name the triangle by its angles and its side lengths.

3.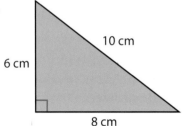
6 cm
10 cm
8 cm

4.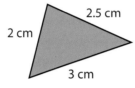
2 cm
2.5 cm
3 cm

5.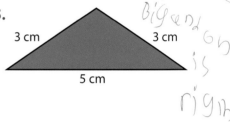
3 cm
3 cm
5 cm

Draw.

6. Use a ruler and an index card to draw an obtuse scalene triangle.

7. Use a ruler to draw an equilateral triangle.

8. Use a ruler to draw an acute isosceles triangle.

Choose the answer.

9. Which best describes an equilateral triangle?

   A. All sides are the same length; all angles have the same measure.

   B. Two sides are the same length; one angle measures 90°.

   C. Two sides are the same length; all angles measure less than 90°.

   D. Two sides are the same length; one angle measures greater than 90°.

10. Which best describes a right isosceles triangle?

   A. Two sides are the same length; one angle measures 90°.

   B. All sides are the same length; two angles measure 90°.

   C. All sides are different lengths; one angle measures 90°.

   D. Two sides are the same length; one angle measures greater than 90°.

T R Y   I T

11. Which triangle always has 1 right angle and 2 sides the same length?

   A. acute isosceles

   B. right isosceles

   C. right equilateral

   D. acute scalene

12. Which triangle always has all sides different lengths and all angles measuring less than 90°?

   A. obtuse equilateral

   B. acute scalene

   C. equilateral

   D. obtuse isosceles

13. Which seems to best describe this triangle?

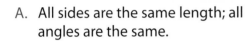

   A. All sides are the same length; all angles are the same.

   B. Two sides are the same length; one angle measures 90°.

   C. Two sides are the same length; all angles are less than 90°.

   D. Two sides are the same length; one angle is obtuse.

14. Which appears to be an equilateral triangle?

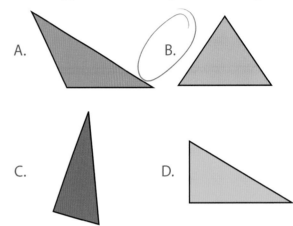

   A.

   B.

   C.

   D.

15. Which name correctly classifies this triangle?

3 in.   3 in.

2.5 in.

   A. acute isosceles

   B. obtuse equilateral

   C. acute scalene

   D. obtuse isosceles

16. Which name correctly classifies this triangle?

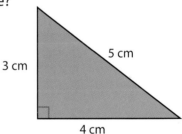

3 cm   5 cm

4 cm

   A. right isosceles

   B. obtuse equilateral

   C. acute scalene

   D. right scalene

TRY IT

Define and Sketch Quadrilaterals (A)

Identify Quadrilaterals

Answer the question.

1. How are these two shapes alike and how are they different?

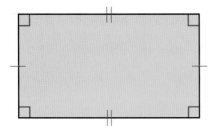 

2. How are these two shapes alike and how are they different?

 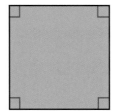

Read the problem and follow the directions.

3. Use a ruler to draw a parallelogram and a trapezoid. Explain how these two shapes are alike and how they are different.

4. Use a ruler to draw a rectangle and a square. Explain how these two shapes are alike and how they are different.

Choose the answer.

5. Which shape has one pair of opposite sides that are parallel but not equal in length?

   A. parallelogram

   B. square

   C. trapezoid

   D. rhombus

6. Which statement is true for all rectangles?

   A. All sides are equal in length.

   B. All angles are right angles.

   C. All angles are acute.

   D. Two angles are obtuse and two angles are acute.

TRY IT

7. Which best describes this quadrilateral?

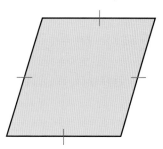

A. polygon with all right angles

B. polygon with exactly one pair of sides that are equal in length

C. polygon with exactly one pair of parallel sides

D. polygon with four sides that are equal in length

8. Which shape has opposite sides that are both equal in length and parallel?

A. triangle

B. trapezoid

C. pentagon

D. parallelogram

9. Which shape has 4 congruent sides?

A. circle

B. trapezoid

C. rhombus

D. triangle

10. Choose **all** the names that could be used to classify this shape.

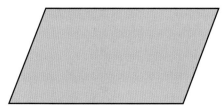

A. quadrilateral

B. trapezoid

C. parallelogram

D. rectangle

11. Choose **all** the names that could be used to classify this shape.

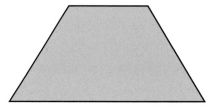

A. rhombus

B. parallelogram

C. quadrilateral

D. trapezoid

TRY IT

Identify Diameters and Radii of Circles

Radius, Diameter, and Circumference

If you know the length of the radius of a circle, you can find its diameter. If you know the length of a diameter of a circle, you can find its radius. If you know the diameter of a circle, you can also estimate its circumference.

PROBLEM Use the circle to answer the questions. If the length of the diameter, line segment *PR* or $\overline{PR}$ of the circle is 14 cm, what is its radius? What is the approximate circumference of the circle?

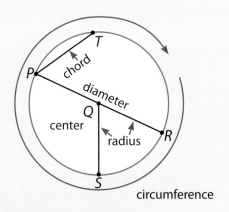

SOLUTION

UNDERSTAND THE PROBLEM Review the terms *radius, diameter,* and *circumference*. Use the length of the diameter to find its radius. Next use the length of the diameter of the circle to estimate its circumference.

DEVISE A PLAN Break this multistep problem into simpler parts.

1 Find the radius of the circle.

- A *radius* is a segment that has one endpoint at the center of the circle and the other endpoint on the circle. Examples are $\overline{QP}$, $\overline{QS}$, and $\overline{QR}$.

- A *diameter* is a segment that passes through the center of the circle and has both its endpoints on the circle. A diameter is formed by two radii (plural of radius).

- The diameter of a circle is two times the length of its radius. So the radius is one-half of the length of the diameter of the circle.

- To find the radius of this circle, write a number sentence to find half of 14 cm or 14 cm divided by 2. Then solve.

LEARN

2 Find the circumference of the circle.

- The *circumference* of the circle is the distance around the circle. The circumference is a little more than 3 times the length of the diameter of the circle.

- To find the circumference, write a number sentence to find 3 times 14 cm. Then solve.

CARRY OUT THE PLAN Break this multistep problem into simpler parts.

1 14 cm ÷ 2 = ?; 14 cm ÷ 2 = 7 cm. So the radius of the circle is 7 cm.

2 14 cm × 3 = ?; 14 cm × 3 = 42 cm. So the circumference of the circle is a little more that 42 cm, or approximately 42 cm.

LOOK BACK Make sure you've answered the questions that were asked. Since the radius is one-half of the length of the diameter, you know the radius must be less than the diameter. Since the circumference is a little more than 3 times the diameter, you know the circumference must be larger than the diameter. Check to see that your answers are reasonable.

ANSWER The radius of the circle is 7 cm, or $r = 7$ cm. The circumference of the circle is a little more than 42 cm.

Answer the question.

1. What part of the circle is segment *AC*?

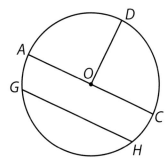

LEARN

Read the problem and follow the directions.

2. Describe the circumference of a circle. Then trace the circumferences of three different circles on the dartboard with your finger.

Solve.

3. The length of the diameter of this circle is 3 inches. What is the length of the radius?

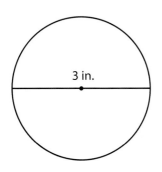

3 in.

4. What is the length of the diameter of this pizza?

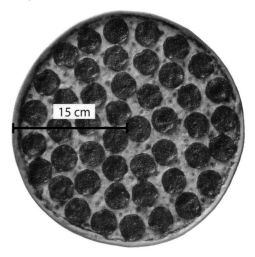

15 cm

5. The diameter of this circle is 5 inches. About how many inches is the circle's circumference?

6. The diameter of the dart board is 18 inches. About how many inches is the circumference of the dart board?

18 in.

Congruent Figures

Find Exact Matches

Worked Examples

Congruent figures are plane figures that have the same shape and size, regardless of their position. If you can slide, turn, or flip figures so that they fit exactly over one another, then the figures are congruent.

PROBLEM Which two figures are congruent? Explain your answer.

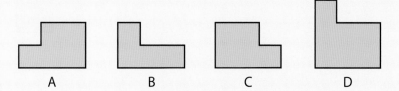

A   B   C   D

SOLUTION

UNDERSTAND THE PROBLEM Find out which two figures have exactly the same shape and size.

DEVISE A PLAN

1 Find two figures that look as if they are exactly the same shape and size. Then trace and cut out one of those two figures.

2 Next slide, turn, or flip the cutout figure so that it fits exactly over one of the other figures.

CARRY OUT THE PLAN

1 Identify the two figures that look congruent. Then trace and cut out one of them. Since Figure A and Figure C look congruent, you can trace and cut out Figure A.

2 Next flip Figure A so that it fits over Figure C with all edges matching exactly.

LOOK BACK Make sure you've answered the question that was asked. Since Figures A and C fit exactly over each other, they have the same shape and size. So Figures A and C are congruent and the answer makes sense.

ANSWER Figure A and Figure C are congruent figures. First I found for two figures that appeared congruent, Figures A and C. Then I traced and cut out Figure A. I flipped Figure A and placed it on top of Figure C. The two figures fit exactly with all edges matching. So I knew they were the same shape and size, or congruent figures.

Choose the two congruent figures.

1.

A.
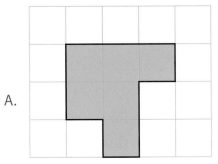

B.
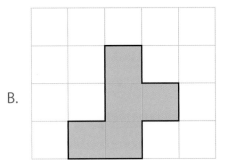

C.
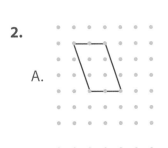

D.
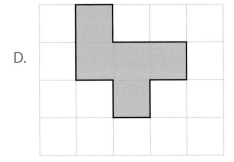

2.

A.

B.

C.

D.
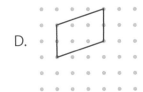

3.

A.

B.
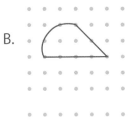

C.

D.

LEARN

4.

A.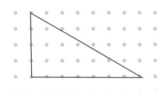

B.

C.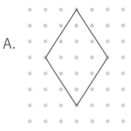

D.

5.

A.

B.

C.

D.

L E A R N

Congruent Figures

Explain Congruent and Similar Figures

Read the problem and follow the directions.

1. Are these two figures congruent? Explain your answer.

2. Explain what makes the following figures similar, but not congruent.

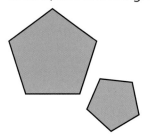

3. Are these two triangles congruent? Explain your answer.

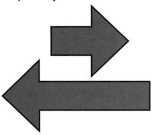

4. Are these two trapezoids congruent? Explain your answer.

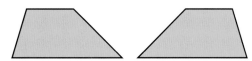

Choose the answer.

5. Look at the two quadrilaterals. Which statement is true?

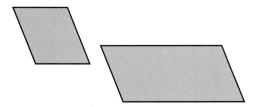

   A. The quadrilaterals are congruent because they are both parallelograms.

   B. The quadrilaterals are not congruent because they have different shapes.

   C. The quadrilaterals are congruent because if you turn one, they will match exactly.

   D. The quadrilaterals are similar but not congruent.

6. Look at the two triangles. Which statement is true?

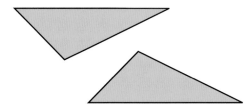

   A. The two figures are not congruent because they are different shapes.

   B. The two figures are not congruent because they are the same shape but not the same size.

   C. The two figures are congruent because they are the same size and shape.

   D. The two figures are similar, but not congruent.

7. Which shape is congruent to this blue shape?

A.

B.

C.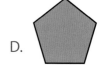

D.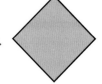

8. Which shape is congruent to this blue shape?

A.

B.

C.

D.

9. Which shape is congruent to this blue shape?

A.

B.

C.

D.

10. Which shape is congruent to this blue shape?

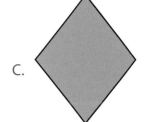

A.

B.

C.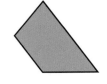

D.

TRY IT

11. Look at the two parallelograms. Which statement is true?

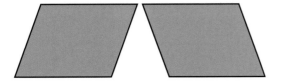

A. The two parallelograms are congruent because one parallelogram was flipped, and it exactly matches the other one.

B. The two parallelograms are not congruent.

C. The two parallelograms are congruent because one parallelogram was slid, and it exactly matches the other one.

12. Look at the two rectangles. Which statement is true?

A. The two rectangles are congruent because one rectangle was slid, and it exactly matches the other one.

B. The two rectangles are not congruent.

C. The two rectangles are congruent because one rectangle was flipped, and it exactly matches the other one.

13. Look at the two rectangles. Which statement is true?

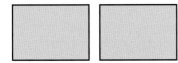

A. The two shapes are congruent because they are the same size and the same shape.

B. The two shapes are not congruent because they are the same size but not the same shape.

C. The two shapes are not congruent because they are the same shape but not the same size.

14. Look at the two shapes. Which statement is true?

A. The two shapes are not congruent because they are the same size but not the same shape.

B. The two shapes are not congruent because they are the same shape but not the same size.

C. The two shapes are congruent because they are the same size and the same shape.

TRY IT

Two Kinds of Symmetry

Different Kinds of Symmetry

Worked Examples

There are two kinds of symmetry. When a plane figure is folded along one or more lines so that the outside boundaries fit exactly on top of each other, the figure has *line symmetry*. When a plane figure is rotated 360° around its center point so that its outside boundaries realign at least once between the start and end of the turn, the figure has *rotational symmetry*.

PROBLEM 1 Does the figure below have line symmetry? If yes, sketch its line or lines of symmetry. If no, explain why there is no line of symmetry.

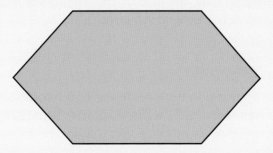

SOLUTION

UNDERSTAND THE PROBLEM Decide if the figure can be folded along one or more lines so that its outside boundaries match exactly. Draw the line or lines of symmetry, or explain why you cannot draw a line of symmetry.

DEVISE A PLAN Trace the figure on a sheet of paper. Then fold and refold the shape until the outside boundaries fit exactly on top of each other. Then draw the figure and the line of symmetry or lines of symmetry that you found, or explain why the figure has no line of symmetry.

CARRY OUT THE PLAN

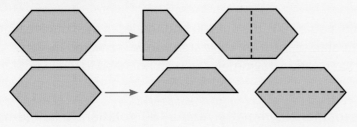

L E A R N

LOOK BACK Since you can draw at least one line of symmetry, the figure has line symmetry. Make sure you've answered the yes-or-no question. Then draw the figure and the lines of symmetry. You do not need to write an explanation.

ANSWER Yes, the figure has line symmetry.

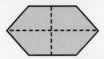

PROBLEM 2 Does the figure have rotational symmetry? If yes, state the degree of the rotation and the fraction of the turn at each location. If no, explain why not.

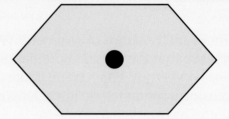

SOLUTION

UNDERSTAND THE PROBLEM Decide if the figure can be rotated 360° around its center point so that its outside boundaries align exactly. For each place this happens, name the rotation by the degree measure and by the fraction of a turn. If the figure does not have rotational symmetry, explain why not.

DEVISE A PLAN
- Trace the figure on a sheet of paper.

- Then push your pencil tip through the center and begin rotating the figure through a quarter turn (90°), a half turn (180°), a three-quarter turn (270°), and end at a full turn (360°).

- Before the shape has made one full turn, look for a place where the figure looks the same as it did before the rotation began.

- Name each point at which the figure has rotational symmetry, or explain why the figure does not have rotational symmetry.

CARRY OUT THE PLAN

   0°   90°   180°   270°   360°

LOOK BACK When you rotate the figure 180°, the outside boundaries of the figure realign so it looks the same as it did at the start of the turn. Make sure you've answered the yes-or-no question. Since the figure has rotational symmetry, you do not need to write an explanation.

ANSWER Yes, the figure has rotational symmetry. After a 180° rotation, or half turn, it looks the same as it did at the start.

Write Yes if the figure has line symmetry and No if it doesn't.
If yes, trace the shape and draw the line or lines of symmetry.

1.

2.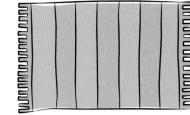

3.

4.

Draw the figure.

5. Draw a triangle that has no lines of symmetry.

6. Draw a triangle that has 1 line of symmetry.

7. Draw a triangle that has 3 lines of symmetry.

8. Draw a shape that has both line symmetry and rotational symmetry.

Write Yes if the figure has line symmetry and No if it doesn't.

9.

10.

11.

12.

L E A R N

Two Kinds of Symmetry

Find Symmetry

Choose the answer.

1. Which figure has line symmetry?

A.    B.    C.   D.

2. Which figure has rotational symmetry?

A.   B.    C.   D.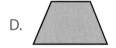

3. Which figure has rotational symmetry?

A.    B.   C.    D.

4. Which picture has rotational symmetry?

A.    B.

C. 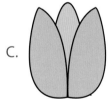   D.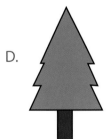

TRY IT

5. How many lines of symmetry does this rectangle have?

A. 0

B. 2

C. 3

D. 4

6. How many lines of symmetry does this square have?

A. 6

B. 5

C. 4

D. 3

7. How many lines of symmetry does this butterfly have?

A. 1

B. 2

C. 4

D. 6

8. How many lines of symmetry does this letter have?

A. 0

B. 1

C. 2

D. 4

TRY IT

Describe Geometric Solids

Faces, Vertices, and Edges

The number of faces, edges, and vertices are often used to identify and describe geometric solids. The number of faces, edges, and vertices of a solid are also related in other ways.

PROBLEM Count the number of faces, vertices, and edges of the solid shown. Record your answers on the data table.

Solid	Number of Faces	Number of Vertices	Number of Edges
cube	?	?	?

SOLUTION

1 Number of faces: Count, one by one, all the flat surfaces, or faces, of the cube. There are 6 faces.

2 Number of vertices: Count, one by one, the number of points where 3 or more edges of the cube meet. There are 8 vertices.

3 Number of edges: Count, one by one, where 2 faces of the cube meet. There are 12 edges.

Also, if you know two of your values, you can find the third value by using the equation $F + V - 2 = E$, where F is the number of faces, V is the number of vertices, and E is the number of edges.

ANSWER 6 faces, 8 vertices, 12 edges

Complete the chart. Count the bases of a prism and the base of a pyramid as *faces* of the geometric solids.

	Solid	Number of Faces	Number of Vertices	Number of Edges
1.	rectangular prism	?	?	?
2.	triangular prism	?	?	?
3.	hexagonal prism	?	?	?
4.	octagonal prism	?	?	?
5.	square pyramid	?	?	?
6.	triangular pyramid	?	?	?

L E A R N

Describe Geometric Solids

Cylinders, Cones, and Spheres

The number of faces, edges, and vertices are often used to identify and describe many geometric solids. A *face* is a flat surface of a solid figure. An *edge* is the boundary where two faces meet or where a face and a curved surface meet. A *vertex* (plural: vertices) is the point at which 3 or more edges meet. The point of a cone is also a *vertex*.

PROBLEM 1 How many faces does a cone have? How many vertices? How many edges?

SOLUTION

1 Number of faces: The cone has 1 flat surface, so it has 1 face.

2 Number of vertices: The figure is a cone. The point of a cone is its vertex, so it has 1 vertex.

3 Number of edges: The face of the cone is a circle that meets a curved surface. Where the face and the curved surface meet is the edge of the cone. The cone has 1 edge.

ANSWER A cone has 1 face, 1 vertex, and 1 edge.

Complete the chart.

	Solid	Number of Faces	Number of Vertices	Number of Edges
1.	cylinder	?	?	?
2.	cone	?	?	?
3.	sphere	?	?	?

L E A R N

Geometric Nets

Sketch Nets

Worked Examples

A net is made by "opening" a solid figure and laying flat its faces. When a net is refolded, it should make the original three-dimensional figure.

PROBLEM Sketch the net of the square pyramid below. You may use the incomplete net on the right to help you.

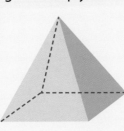 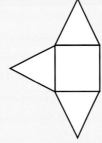

SOLUTION

1 Describe all the faces of the square pyramid, even those you cannot see. There are 4 triangles and 1 square base. Each triangle is touching 1 side of the pyramid's square base.

2 Visualize what the net would look like if it were opened at the vertex where the triangles meet and then unfolded to lie flat. Sketch the net.

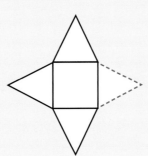

ANSWER

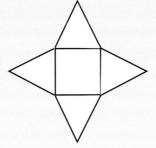

L E A R N

Look at the solid figure and its partial net. Sketch the completed net.

1. triangular prism

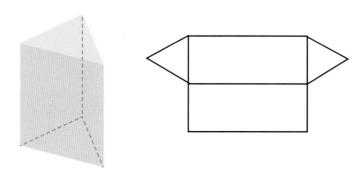

2. cylinder

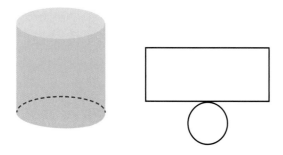

**Complete the net so it could be folded to form a solid figure.
Name the figure.**

3.

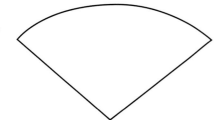

4.

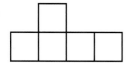

5.

LEARN

Geometric Nets

Identify Nets

Write the name of the 3-D figure that the net represents.

1.

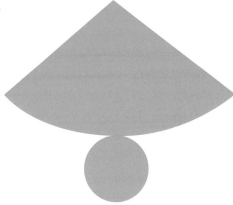

2.

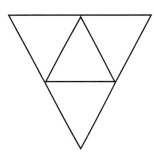

Read the problem and follow the directions.

3. Complete this net so it can be folded to form a cube.

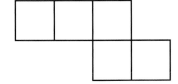

4. Complete this net so it can be folded to form a triangular prism.

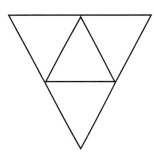

TRY IT

5. Sketch a net of a cube, making a different net from the net in Problem 3.

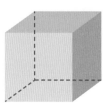

6. Sketch a net of a square pyramid.

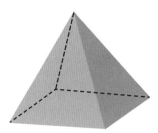

Choose the net of the 3-D figure.

7.

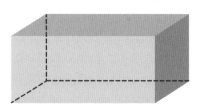

A.

B.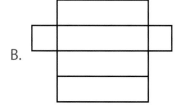

C.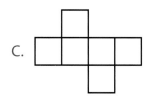

8.

A.

B.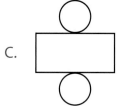

C.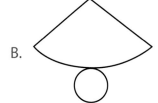

TRY IT

Count with Negative Numbers (A)

Count Backward and Forward

Worked Examples

You can identify a pattern to find the missing numbers in a number sequence. First figure out how much the given numbers increase or decrease. Then apply this pattern to complete the sequence.

PROBLEM What numbers are missing in this number sequence?

$^-12, ^-10, ^-8, \underline{\;\,?\,\;}, \underline{\;\,?\,\;}, ^-2, 0, ^+2$

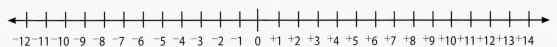

SOLUTION

1 Decide whether the number sequence is counting forward or backward. This sequence is counting forward.

2 Determine what the pattern is. This pattern is "count forward by 2s."

3 Find the starting number on a number line. Count forward, following the pattern. Use your finger to help keep track of the jumps. When you get to the first missing number, look at where your finger is on the number line. Write the missing number.

4 Continue counting till you reach the end of the number sequence. Use the number line to find any missing numbers.

5 To check your answer, show the complete pattern on the number line.

ANSWER The missing numbers are $^-6$ and $^-4$.

Answer the question.

1. What is the next number in this pattern?

$^+6, ^+3, 0, ^-3, ^-6, \underline{\;\,?\,\;}$

L E A R N

2. The numbers in this pattern increase by the same amount each time.
    What are the next three numbers in the pattern?

    $^-11, ^-9, ^-7, ^-5, ^-3,$ __?__, __?__, __?__

3. Serena is counting backward by 8s. If she starts counting at 16,
    what two numbers are missing?

    $^+16, ^+8, 0, ^-8,$ __?__, __?__, $^-32$

Read the problem and follow the directions.

4. Count backward by 5s from $^+20$ to $^-25$ and write your number sequence.

5. Count forward by 4s from $^-20$ to $^+4$ and write your number sequence.

LEARN

Count with Negative Numbers (A)

Find Missing Numbers

Read the problem and follow the directions.

1. Count backward by 3s from $^+6$ to $^-15$ and write the number sequence.

2. Count forward by 2s from $^-13$ to $^-1$ and write the number sequence.

3. Count backward by 2s from $^+7$ to $^-11$ and write your number sequence.

4. Count forward by 5s from $^-25$ to $^+15$ and write your number sequence.

Answer the question.

5. The numbers in this pattern decrease by the same amount each time. What are the next three numbers in the pattern?

   $^+10, 0, ^-10, ^-20, ^-30, \underline{\ ?\ }, \underline{\ ?\ }, \underline{\ ?\ }$

6. Rosa is counting by 6s. If she starts counting at $^-18$, what two numbers are missing?

   $^-18, ^-12, \underline{\ ?\ }, \underline{\ ?\ }, ^+6, ^+12, ^+18$

Choose the answer.

7. What is the next integer in this pattern?

   $^+15, ^+10, ^+5, 0, ^-5, ^-10, \underline{\ ?\ }$

A. $^-5$	B. $^-20$
C. $^-15$	D. $^+5$

8. What is the next integer in this pattern?

   $^+6, ^+4, ^+2, 0, ^-2, ^-4, ^-6, \underline{\ ?\ }$

A. $^-2$	B. $^-8$
C. $^+2$	D. $^-4$

9. Which integer is missing in this pattern?

   $^+7, ^+3, ^-1, \underline{\ ?\ }, ^-9, ^-13$

A. $^-5$	B. $^-3$
C. $^+4$	D. $^-4$

10. What is the next integer in this pattern?

    $^+11, ^+7, ^+3, ^-1, ^-5, ^-9, \underline{\ ?\ }$

A. $^-13$	B. $^-4$
C. $^-10$	D. $^+4$

11. Which integer is missing in this pattern?

    $11, 6, 1, ^-4, \underline{\ ?\ }, ^-14, ^-19$

A. $^-5$	B. $^-9$
C. $^-11$	D. $^+5$

TRY IT

Count with Negative Numbers (B)

Predict Number Patterns

Worked Examples

You can predict a missing number in a counting pattern that has negative numbers.

PROBLEM The numbers in this pattern decrease by the same amount each time. What is the 10th number in the pattern?

$^-16, ^-18, ^-20, ^-22, ^-24, \underline{\ ?\ }, \underline{\ ?\ }, \underline{\ ?\ }, \underline{\ ?\ }, \underline{\ ?\ }$

SOLUTION

1 Write the sequence.

2 Decide whether the number sequence is counting forward or backward. This sequence is counting backward.

3 Determine what the pattern is. This pattern is "count backward by 2s."

4 Count backward from the starting number, following the pattern. For this problem, start with $^-16$, count back by 2, and the next number is $^-18$.

5 Continue counting backward. When you get to the first missing number, write that number ($^-26$).

6 Repeat Step 5 to find the remaining missing numbers: $^-28, ^-30, ^-32, ^-34$.

7 Look at the 10th number to get your answer.

8 To check your answer, make sure all the numbers in the sequence follow the pattern.

ANSWER The 10th number is $^-34$.

Find the missing numbers.

1. The numbers in this pattern decrease by the same amount each time. What are the next three numbers in the pattern?

   $^-8, ^-12, ^-16, ^-20, ^-24, \underline{\ ?\ }, \underline{\ ?\ }, \underline{\ ?\ }$

2. Steve is counting backward by 6s. If he starts counting at $^+6$, what are the next three numbers in this pattern?

$^+6, 0, ^-6, ^-12, ^-18, \underline{?}, \underline{?}, \underline{?}$

3. Amy is counting backward by 7s. If she starts counting at $^+49$, what is the 12th number in the pattern?

$^+49, ^+42, ^+35, ^+28, ^+21, ^+14, \underline{?}, \underline{?}, \underline{?}, \underline{?}, \underline{?}, \underline{?}$

4. What is the 8th number in this pattern?

$^-18, ^-16, ^-14, ^-12, \underline{?}, \underline{?}, \underline{?}, \underline{?}$

5. What is the 10th number in this pattern?

$^-11, ^-9, ^-7, ^-5, ^-3, ^-1, ^+1, \underline{?}, \underline{?}, \underline{?}$

6. What are the missing numbers in the pattern?

$^-20, ^-15, ^-10, \underline{?}, \underline{?}, \underline{?}, ^+10, ^+15$

7. What is the missing number in the pattern?

$^-7, ^-4, \underline{?}, ^+2, ^+5, ^+8, ^+11$

8. What is the missing number in this pattern?

$^-30, ^-27, ^-24, ^-21, ^-18, \underline{?}$

Write a pattern problem.

9. Write a number-pattern problem that starts with a positive number and decreases so that the 10th number is negative.

L E A R N

Count with Negative Numbers (B)

Solve Problems with Number Patterns

Find the missing numbers.

1. The numbers in this pattern increase by the same amount each time. What are the next three numbers in the pattern? $^-27, ^-24, ^-21, ^-18, \underline{\ ?\ }, \underline{\ ?\ }, \underline{\ ?\ }$

2. Derek is counting backward by 4s. If he starts counting at $^+20$, what two numbers are missing? $^+20, ^+16, ^+12, ^+8, \underline{\ ?\ }, 0, ^-4, \underline{\ ?\ }, ^-12, ^-16$

Predict the number.

3. Rebecca is counting backward by 10s. If she starts counting at $^+40$, what is the 10th number in the pattern?
$^+40, ^+30, ^+20, ^+10, 0, ^-10, \underline{\ ?\ }, \underline{\ ?\ }, \underline{\ ?\ }, \underline{\ ?\ }$

4. What is the 12th number in this pattern?
$^-45, ^-50, ^-55, ^-60, ^-65, \underline{\ ?\ }, \underline{\ ?\ }, \underline{\ ?\ }, \underline{\ ?\ }, \underline{\ ?\ }, \underline{\ ?\ }, \underline{\ ?\ }$

5. What is the 15th number in this pattern?
$^-20, ^-18, ^-16, ^-14, ^-12, ^-10, ^-8, ^-6, \underline{\ ?\ }, \underline{\ ?\ }, \underline{\ ?\ }, \underline{\ ?\ }, \underline{\ ?\ }, \underline{\ ?\ }, \underline{\ ?\ }$

Choose the answer.

6. What is the 10th number in this pattern?

$^+14, ^+7, 0, ^-7, ^-14, \underline{\ ?\ }, \underline{\ ?\ }, \underline{\ ?\ }, \underline{\ ?\ }, \underline{\ ?\ }$

  A. $^-7$ B. $^-28$

  C. $^-42$ D. $^-49$

7. What is the 12th number in this pattern?

$^+12, ^+10, ^+8, ^+6, ^+4, \underline{\ ?\ }, \underline{\ ?\ }, \underline{\ ?\ }, \underline{\ ?\ }, \underline{\ ?\ }, \underline{\ ?\ }, \underline{\ ?\ }$

  A. $^-14$ B. $^-12$

  C. $^-8$ D. $^-10$

8. What is the 8th number in this pattern?

$^+12, ^+8, ^+4, 0, \underline{\ ?\ }, \underline{\ ?\ }, \underline{\ ?\ }, \underline{\ ?\ }$

  A. $^-12$ B. $^-16$

  C. $^-8$ D. $^-4$

9. What is the 7th number in this pattern?

$36, 24, 12, \underline{\ ?\ }, \underline{\ ?\ }, \underline{\ ?\ }, \underline{\ ?\ }$

  A. $^-12$ C. $^-36$

  B. $^-24$ D. $^-48$

10. What is the 9th number in this pattern?

$^+11, ^+6, ^+1, ^-4, ^-9, ^-14, \underline{\ ?\ }, \underline{\ ?\ }, \underline{\ ?\ }$

  A. $^-15$ B. $^-29$

  C. $^-19$ D. $^-5$

11. What is the 10th number in this pattern?

$^+15, ^+10, ^+5, 0, \underline{\ ?\ }, \underline{\ ?\ }, \underline{\ ?\ }, \underline{\ ?\ }, \underline{\ ?\ }, \underline{\ ?\ }$

  A. $^-30$ B. $^-20$

  C. $^-5$ D. $^-10$

TRY IT

Rational Numbers on a Number Line (B)

Compare Number Location

> ## Worked Examples

You can mark the locations of positive and negative numbers on the same number line and compare their values.

PROBLEM Is $^-2$ located to the left or right of $^-1\frac{1}{4}$? Is $^-2$ greater than $^-1\frac{1}{4}$ or less than $^-1\frac{1}{4}$? Is $^-2$ greater than $^-1.25$ or less than $^-1.25$?

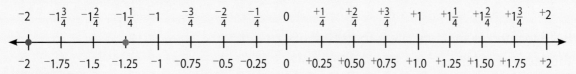

SOLUTION

1 Copy the number line.

2 Use one color marker to plot the point for $^-2$. Use another color marker to plot the point $^-1\frac{1}{4}$.

3 Look at the two points plotted. The point for $^-2$ is to the left of the point for $^-1\frac{1}{4}$. $^-1\frac{1}{4}$ is equivalent to $^-1.25$.

4 Since a number line shows numbers in order, numbers to the left are less than numbers to the right. So $^-2$ is less than $^-1\frac{1}{4}$ and $^-1.25$.

ANSWER Since $^-2$ is located to the left of $^-1\frac{1}{4}$, $^-2$ is less than $^-1\frac{1}{4}$ and its equivalent $^-1.25$.

Use the number line to answer Problems 1 and 2.

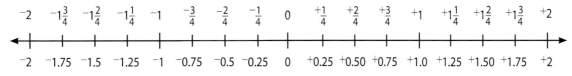

1. Is $\frac{1}{4}$ located to the right of 0.5 or to the left of 0.5?

2. Is $\frac{1}{4}$ greater than 0.5 or is $\frac{1}{4}$ less than 0.5?

L E A R N

Use the number line to answer Problems 3 and 4.

3. Is $^+1$ located to the right of $^-2$ or to the left of $^-2$?

4. Is $^+1$ greater than $^-2$ or is $^+1$ less than $^-2$?

Use the number line to answer Problems 5 and 6.

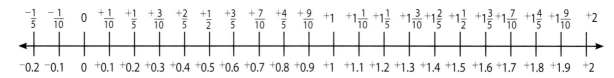

5. Is 0.3 located to the right of $\frac{3}{10}$, to the left of $\frac{3}{10}$, or in the same position as $\frac{3}{10}$ on the number line?

6. Is 0.3 greater than $\frac{3}{10}$, less than $\frac{3}{10}$, or equal to $\frac{3}{10}$?

Use the number line to answer Problems 7 and 8.

| $-\frac{1}{5}$ | $-\frac{1}{10}$ | 0 | $+\frac{1}{10}$ | $+\frac{1}{5}$ | $+\frac{3}{10}$ | $+\frac{2}{5}$ | $+\frac{1}{2}$ | $+\frac{3}{5}$ | $+\frac{7}{10}$ | $+\frac{4}{5}$ | $+\frac{9}{10}$ | $+1$ | $+1\frac{1}{10}$ | $+1\frac{1}{5}$ | $+1\frac{3}{10}$ | $+1\frac{2}{5}$ | $+1\frac{1}{2}$ | $+1\frac{3}{5}$ | $+1\frac{7}{10}$ | $+1\frac{4}{5}$ | $+1\frac{9}{10}$ | $+2$ |

$^-0.2$ $^-0.1$ 0 $^+0.1$ $^+0.2$ $^+0.3$ $^+0.4$ $^+0.5$ $^+0.6$ $^+0.7$ $^+0.8$ $^+0.9$ $^+1$ $^+1.1$ $^+1.2$ $^+1.3$ $^+1.4$ $^+1.5$ $^+1.6$ $^+1.7$ $^+1.8$ $^+1.9$ $^+2$

7. Is $^-0.1$ located to the right of $^-0.2$ or to the left of $^-0.2$?

8. Is $^-0.1$ greater than $^-0.2$ or less than $^-0.2$?

LEARN

Rational Numbers on a Number Line (C)

Work with Number Lines

Worked Examples

You can use what you know about integers, fractions, and decimal numbers to locate a point on a number line.

PROBLEM Which number line shows a point at $+\frac{3}{5}$?

A.
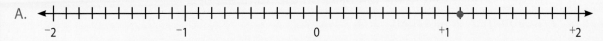

B.
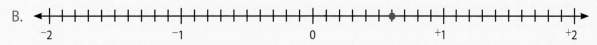

C.
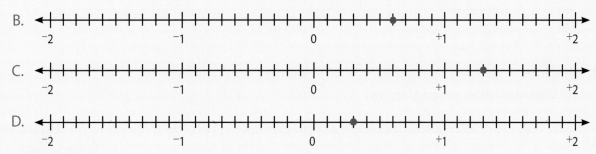

D.
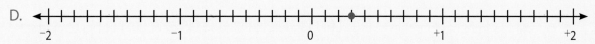

SOLUTION

UNDERSTAND THE PROBLEM Choose the number line that shows a point to the right of 0 that is $\frac{3}{5}$ the distance from 0 to $+1$.

DEVISE A PLAN Use logical reasoning. Look at the number lines and rule out any number line that doesn't show a point at $+\frac{3}{5}$. Look at the remaining number line. Make sure it shows the point at $+\frac{3}{5}$.

CARRY OUT THE PLAN Think: $+\frac{3}{5}$ is a fraction between 0 and $+1$, so the points in A and C cannot be correct because they both show points to the right of $+1$, or greater than $+1$. The point in D is $\frac{3}{10}$ the distance from 0 to $+1$, not $\frac{3}{5}$ the distance.

The point in B is $\frac{6}{10}$ the distance from 0 to $+1$. Since $\frac{6 \div 2}{10 \div 2} = +\frac{3}{5}$, the correct answer is B.

L E A R N

Read the problem and follow the directions.

1. Sketch a number line and graph $^-3$, $^+1$, and $^+2.5$ on the number line.

Answer the question.

2. The integer $^-2$ is located to the left of $^+1$ on the number line.
    Is $^-2$ greater than or less than $^+2$?

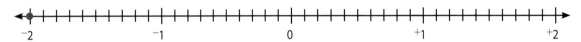

3. The integer $^-2$ is located to the right of $^-5$ on the number line.
    Is $^-2$ greater than or less than $^-5$?

Choose the answer.

4. Which number line shows a point at $^+0.25$?

A.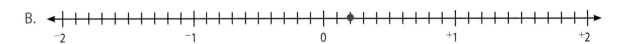

B.

C.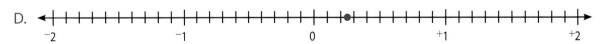

D.

5. Which number line shows $^+1$, $^+1.75$, and $^+\frac{3}{10}$?

A.
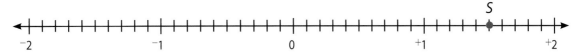

B.

C.

D.

6. Point *S* represents $^+1.5$ on this number line. Which statement is true about the location of $^+1\frac{1}{5}$ on this number line?

A. $^+1\frac{1}{5}$ is at the same point as point *S*.

B. $^+1\frac{1}{5}$ is to the right of point *S*.

C. $^+1\frac{1}{5}$ is to the left of point *S*.

D. You cannot determine the location of $^+1\frac{1}{5}$ on the number line.

LEARN

Expressions and Equations

Algebraic Expressions and Equations

Worked Examples

You can use variables to write algebraic expressions or equations that match different descriptions. You can use any symbol to stand for the unknown number. For example, you can use a triangle (▲) for the variable.

PROBLEM 1 Write an *expression* that matches this situation:

Katherine separates a pile of photos into five equal groups.

SOLUTION

UNDERSTAND THE PROBLEM
You are separating an unknown number of photos into 5 equal groups, or dividing an unknown number by 5.

DEVISE A PLAN Use (▲) to stand for the unknown number of photos.

CARRY OUT THE PLAN
$▲ \div 5$

LOOK BACK Make sure you've answered what was asked. Katherine separates photos into 5 equal groups, so the following expression makes sense: $▲ \div 5$.

ANSWER $▲ \div 5$

PROBLEM 2 Write an *equation* that matches this situation:

Leo had some batteries and then bought six more. He has thirteen batteries now.

SOLUTION

UNDERSTAND THE PROBLEM
"Bought six more" means addition, so you are adding 6 to an unknown number of batteries. "He has thirteen batteries now" means "equals 13."

DEVISE A PLAN Use (▲) to stand for the unknown number of batteries.

CARRY OUT THE PLAN
$▲ + 6 = 13$

LOOK BACK Make sure you've answered what was asked. Leo had some batteries and bought 6 more for a total of 13 batteries. So the following equation makes sense: $▲ + 6 = 13$.

ANSWER $▲ + 6 = 13$

LEARN

Read the situation. Use a triangle (▲) for the variable and explain what the variable represents. Then write the algebraic expression or equation that matches the situation.

1. Toby has three times as many trading cards as Ruth.
   Toby has twenty-four cards.

2. Joe bought a bag of chips.
   He ate twelve of them.
   He has eight chips left.

3. Amy has six stacks of CDs with the same number of CDs in each stack.

Read the situation. Use a question mark (?) for the variable and explain what the variable represents. Then write the algebraic expression or equation that matches the situation.

4. Jill walks five blocks to the library and then continues on to the grocery store.
   She walks a total of fifteen blocks.

5. Nathan has thirty party favors to divide among each of his friends.

Read the situation. Use a *p* for the variable and explain what the variable represents. Then write the algebraic expression or equation that matches the situation.

6. Lizzy scored twelve points in each basketball game this season.
   She scored a total of eighty-four points.

7. Adam had a bag of rocks.
   He lost eleven of them.
   He now has twenty-five rocks.

LEARN

Expressions and Equations

Expressions and Equations Practice

Read the problem or situation. Then write the expression or equation that matches the situation. To represent an unknown number, use a symbol or letter.

1. Write an expression that means twelve times an unknown number.

2. Lisa took twenty-five pictures on her digital camera. She deleted twelve of them. She then had thirteen pictures left on her camera. Write an equation that represents this situation.

3. Write an expression that represents the following:
   Jack had some peanuts in a bag. He ate nine of the peanuts.

4. Write an equation that represents the following:
   Janet has many pairs of shoes. She bought three more pairs. She now has sixteen pairs of shoes.

5. Write an expression that represents the following:
   There are 5 flowers in each of 6 vases.

Choose the answer.

6. Which expression means 9 more than a number?

   A. $n + 9$
   B. $9 \times n$
   C. $n - 9$
   D. $9 \div n$

7. Which expression means 10 less than a number?

   A. $a + 10$
   B. $10 \times a$
   C. $a - 10$
   D. $10 \div a$

8. Which expression means 12 divided by a number?

   A. $12 \div p$
   B. $p + 12$
   C. $12 \times p$
   D. $p - 12$

9. Candy divides some stamps into 4 equal groups. Which expression represents this situation?

   A. $\blacktriangle - 4$
   B. $4 \times \blacktriangle$
   C. $\blacktriangle \div 4$
   D. $4 + \blacktriangle$

10. Neil has 5 times as many pencils as Victor. Which expression represents this situation?

    A. $\blacktriangle - 5$
    B. $5 \times \blacktriangle$
    C. $\blacktriangle \div 5$
    D. $\blacktriangle + 5$

11. Which equation means that 12 decreased by a number is 4?

    A. $12 - 4 = n$
    B. $12 - n = 4$
    C. $12 + 4 = n$
    D. $4 \times 12 = n$

TRY IT

12. Which equation means a number divided by thirty is equal to 3?

    A. $30 + 3 = e$ B. $e \div 30 = 3$ C. $30 \times e = 3$ D. $30 - 3 = e$

13. Tim walked a number of steps around the park. Then he walked 10 more steps. He walked a total of 25 steps. Which equation represents this situation?

    A. $\square + 10 = 25$ B. $25 \times 10 = \square$ C. $25 + 10 = \square$ D. $10 - \square = 25$

14. Vanessa walked the same number of miles each day for 5 days. She walked a total of 20 miles. Which equation represents this situation?

    A. $20 + 5 = \square$ B. $20 - 5 = \square$ C. $\square \times 5 = 20$ D. $20 \times \square = 5$

15. Manny divided his collection of baseball cards equally among 4 of his friends. Each friend got 5 cards. Which equation represents this situation?

    A. $\square = 4 + 5$ B. $\square = 5 \div 4$ C. $\square \div 4 = 5$ D. $4 \times 5 = \square$

16. Kevin had some money. He spent $8. He has $20 left. Which equation represents this situation?

    A. $20 - \square = 8$ B. $20 - 8 = \square$ C. $\square + 8 = 20$ D. $\square - 8 = 20$

17. Which equation means ten increased by a number equals 22?

    A. $10 + t = 22$ B. $22 + 10 = t$ C. $t - 10 = 22$ D. $t \div 10 = 22$

18. Which equation means twenty divided by a number is equal to 10?

    A. $20 + d = 10$ B. $20 - d = 10$ C. $20 \div d = 10$ D. $20 \times d = 10$

19. James had some apples. He bought 5 more. Which expression represents this situation?

    A. $\blacktriangle - 5$ B. $5 \times \blacktriangle$ C. $\blacktriangle \div 5$ D. $\blacktriangle + 5$

20. Bonnie divides some cherries into 8 equal groups. Which expression represents this situation?

    A. $p - 8$ B. $p \div 8$ C. $p + 8$ D. $8 \times p$

TRY IT

Addition Property of Equality (A)

Complete the Equation

Write the number that should replace the question mark.

1. $5 = 5$
    $3 + 5 = 5 + \underline{}$

2. $9 = 9$
    $6 + 9 = 9 + \underline{}$

3. $8 = 4 + 4$
    $2 + 8 = 4 + 4 + \underline{}$

4. $1 + 6 = 7$
    $4 + 1 + 6 = 7 + \underline{}$

5. $10 = 2 + 8$
    $\underline{} + 10 = 2 + 8 + 9$

Choose the answer.

6. Marian and George have the same number of marbles. Each of them is given 4 more marbles. Which statement is true?

    A. Marian now has 4 more marbles than George.

    B. George now has 4 more marbles than Marian.

    C. Marian and George have the same number of marbles.

7. Darin and Tim have the same number of balloons. Each of them blows up 6 more balloons. Which statement is true?

    A. Darin and Tim have the same number of balloons.

    B. Darin now has 6 more balloons than Tim.

    C. Tim now has 6 more balloons than Darin.

8. Which number could replace the ▲?
    $4 = 4$
    $4 + 9 = ▲ + 4$

    A. 4

    B. 5

    C. 9

    D. 13

9. Which number could replace the ▲?
    $6 + 8 = 10 + 4$
    $6 + 8 + 5 = 10 + 4 + ▲$

    A. 5

    B. 14

    C. 19

    D. 28

TRY IT

Choose the answer. Circle the correct number of objects added to each side.

10. Mark and Carrie found sea stars on the sand. Mark put his sea stars into a pail. Carrie put her sea stars on the table. They each collected the same number of sea stars. Both Mark and Carrie found 3 more sea stars.

Which picture is correct?

11. Dave and Cara had some marbles. Dave put his marbles into a jar. Cara put her marbles on a chair. They each had the same number of marbles. Dave and Cara were each given 4 more marbles.

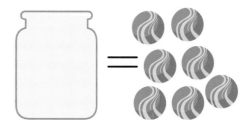

Which picture is correct?

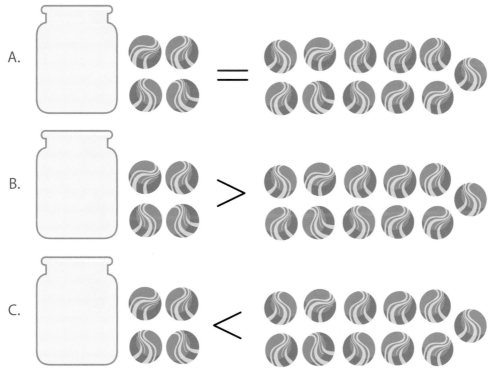

ALGEBRA THINKING

251

ADDITION PROPERTY OF EQUALITY (A)

12. Paula and Martine had some toy cars. Paula put her cars into a box. Martine put her cars on the table. They each had the same number of cars. Both Paula and Martine bought 7 more toy cars.

Which picture is correct?

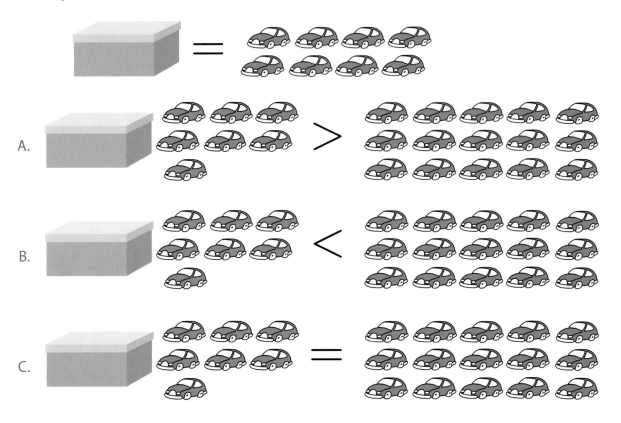

13. Lara and Tom were given some seeds. Tom planted his seeds in a flowerbed. Lara left her seeds in a bowl overnight. They each were given the same number of seeds. Both Lara and Tom were given 3 more seeds.

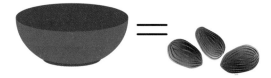

Which picture is correct?

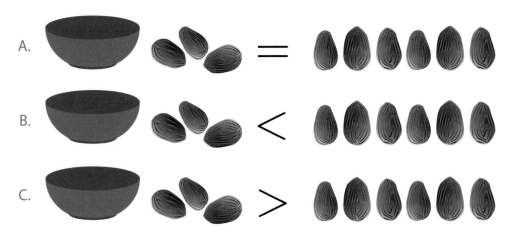

Multiply by Equal Quantities (A)

Create Equal Quantities

Solve.

1. Draw a picture to show how to multiply the equation by 2.

$$7 = 3 + 4$$

2. Use your picture from Problem 1 complete each number sentence.

$$7 = 3 + 4$$
$$2 \times 7 = \square \times (3 + 4)$$
$$2 \times 7 = \square \times 3 + \square \times 4$$
$$2 \times 7 = \square + \square$$
$$14 = \square$$

Answer the question.

3. Which number could replace the $\square$?

$$7 = 7$$
$$\square \times 7 = 7 \times 2$$

4. What is the value of m?

$$m \times 9 \times 8 = 9 \times 8 \times 5$$

Write the number that replaces the $\square$.

5. $$10 = 10$$
$$4 \times 10 = 10 \times \square$$

6. $$2 + 8 = 10$$
$$\square \times (2 + 8) = 5 \times 10$$

7. $$9 + 9 = 18$$
$$(9 + 9) \times \square = 18 \times 3$$

8. $$5 = 5$$
$$5 \times \square = 5 \times 10$$

Choose the answer.

9. Which number could replace the $\square$?

$$6 = 6$$
$$2 \times 6 = \square \times 6$$

  A. 2   B. 6

  C. 12   D. 36

10. What is the value of m?

$$m \times 4 \times 6 = 4 \times 6$$

  A. 1   B. 3

  C. 6   D. 24

TRY IT

11. Elias bought a bag of marbles. He wrote this equation to show the number of marbles in one bag.

$$n = 12$$

If Elias bought 3 bags of marbles, which equation would represent the number of marbles he has now?

A. $3 \times n = 4$

B. $3 \times n = 12$

C. $3 \times n = 15$

D. $3 \times n = 36$

12. Sandra bought a bunch of roses. She wrote this equation to show the number of roses in one bunch.

$$p = 10$$

If Sandra bought 5 bunches of roses, which equation would represent the number of roses she has now?

A. $5 \times p = 60$

B. $5 \times p = 50$

C. $5 \times p = 25$

D. $5 \times p = 15$

13. Which number could replace the ☐?

$$15 = 15$$
$$4 \times 15 = 15 \times \square$$

A. 4   B. 15

C. 60   D. 120

14. Which number could replace the ☐?

$$20 = 20$$
$$\square \times 20 = 20 \times 3$$

A. 3   B. 20

C. 80   D. 100

15. Laura bought 10 red apples last week. Ellen also bought 5 red apples and 5 yellow apples last week. Laura bought 4 times as many apples this week as she did last week. Ellen also bought 4 times as many apples this week as she did last week.

Which statement is true?

A. Ellen bought more apples than Laura.

B. Laura bought more apples than Ellen.

C. Laura and Ellen bought the same number of apples this week.

16. Dario bought 4 notepads last month. Mitch also bought 4 notepads last month. Dario bought 2 times as many notepads this month as he did last month. Mitch also bought 2 times as many notepads as he did last month.

Which statement is true?

A. Dario bought more notepads than Mitch.

B. Mitch and Dario bought the same number of notepads.

C. Mitch bought more notepads than Dario.

TRY IT

Two-Variable Equations (A)

Substitute and Solve

Worked Examples

For equations with two variables: If you know the value of one variable, you can find the value of the other variable.

PROBLEM 1 What is the value of n if $p = 5$?

$n = p + 3 + 11$

SOLUTION

$n = p + 3 + 11$

$n = 5 + 3 + 11$ ⟵ Substitute 5 for p.

$n = 19$ ⟵ Solve for n.

ANSWER The value of n is 19.

PROBLEM 2 What is the value of b if $c = 4$?

$b = 3 \times c + 9$

SOLUTION

$b = 3 \times c + 9$

$b = 3 \times 4 + 9$ ⟵ Substitute 4 for c.

$b = 21$ ⟵ Solve for b.

ANSWER The value of b is 21.

Solve.

1. What is the value of y if $x = 7$?

   $y = 16 - x$

2. If $t = 3$, what is the value of s?

   $s = 8 \times t + 1$

3. If $y = 9$, what is the value of n?

   $4 \times y - 5 = n$

4. What is the value of a if $b = 10$?

   $a = b \times 3 + 2$

5. If $c = 4$, what is the value of d?

   $c \times 2 + 5 = d$

6. What is the value of n if $p = 12$?

   $n = p - 5 - 7$

LEARN

Line Segments in the Coordinate Plane

Horizontal Segment Lengths

Worked Examples

If you know the coordinates of the endpoints of a horizontal line segment, you can use subtraction to find its length.

PROBLEM 1

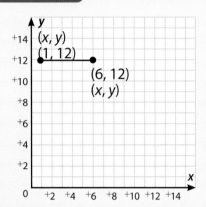

SOLUTION

1. Count the units. Then look for another way to find the length.

2. The difference between the x-coordinates, 6 and 1, also gives the length.

3. $6 - 1 = 5$
So the length is 5 units.

ANSWER The length of the horizontal line segment is 5 units.

PROBLEM 2

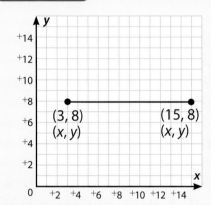

SOLUTION

1. Subtract the x-coordinates, 15 and 3, to find the length. Length is always a positive number.

2. $15 - 3 = 12$
So the length is 12 units.

ANSWER The length of the horizontal line segment is 12 units.

L E A R N

Subtract to find the length of the horizontal line segment.
Write the subtraction equation you used. Then write the length of the
segment in units.

1.

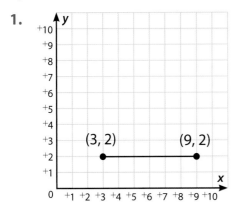

2.

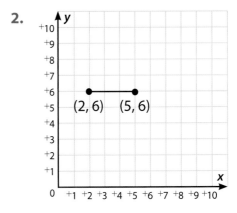

3.

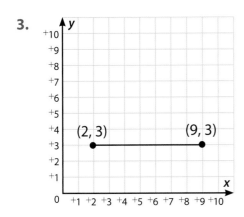

4.

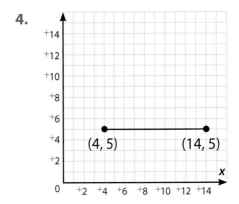

5.

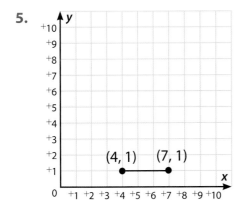

6.

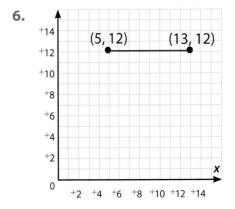

Line Segments in the Coordinate Plane

Vertical Segment Lengths

Worked Examples

If you know the coordinates of the endpoints of a vertical line segment, you can use subtraction to find its length.

PROBLEM 1

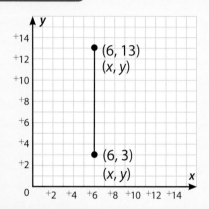

SOLUTION

1. Count the units. Then look for another way to find the length.

2. The difference between the y-coordinates, 13 and 3, also gives the length.

3. $13 - 3 = 10$
   So the length is 10 units.

ANSWER The length of the vertical line segment is 10 units.

PROBLEM 2

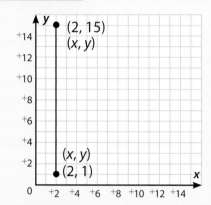

SOLUTION

1. Subtract the y-coordinates, 15 and 1, to find the length. Length is always a positive number.

2. $15 - 1 = 14$
   So the length is 14 units.

ANSWER The length of the vertical line segment is 14 units.

Subtract to find the length of the vertical line segment.
Write the subtraction equation you used. Then write the length of the
segment in units.

1.

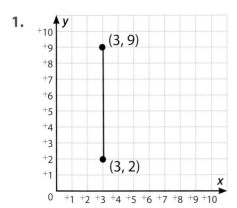

2.

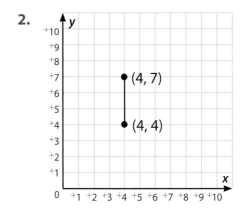

3.

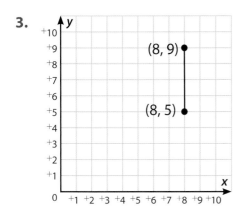

4.

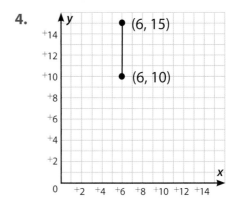

5.

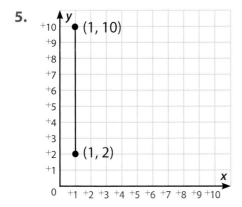

6.

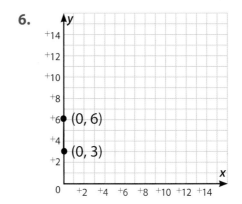

L E A R N

Linear Relationships (A)

Points on a Line

Read the problem and follow the directions.

1. Write the ordered pairs to complete the table.

$y = 3 \times x$		
Input x	Output y	(Input, Output) (x, y)
0	0	?
$^+1$	$^+3$	?
$^+2$	$^+6$	?
$^+3$	$^+9$	?
$^+4$	$^+12$	?
$^+5$	$^+15$	?

2. Complete the input-output table and then plot the points on a coordinate grid.

Rule: Subtract 3		
Input x	Output y	Ordered Pair (x, y)
$^+3$	0	?
$^+4$	$^+1$	?
$^+5$	?	?
$^+6$	?	?
$^+7$	?	?
$^+8$	?	?

TRY IT

Choose the answer.

3. Suketo plotted 3 points from the equation $y = 2 \times x$ on this coordinate grid. He drew a straight line through the points. Which ordered pair would also be on this line?

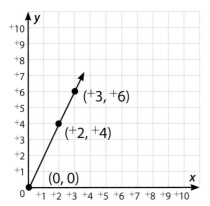

A. $(^+3, ^+8)$

B. $(^+4, ^+6)$

C. $(^+5, ^+10)$

D. $(^+7, ^+7)$

4. Sari plotted 3 points from the equation $y = x + 4$ on this coordinate grid. She drew a straight line through the points. Which ordered pair would also be on this line?

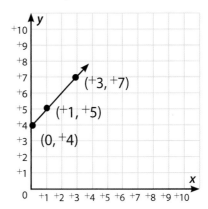

A. $(^+3, ^+9)$

B. $(^+6, ^+7)$

C. $(^+3, ^+6)$

D. $(^+5, ^+9)$

5. Identify the graph that matches the equation in the table.

$y = x + 3$		
Input x	Output y	Ordered Pair (x, y)
0	$^+3$	$(0, ^+3)$
$^+1$	$^+4$	$(^+1, ^+4)$
$^+2$	$^+5$	$(^+2, ^+5)$
$^+3$	$^+6$	$(^+3, ^+6)$
$^+4$	$^+7$	$(^+4, ^+7)$
$^+5$	$^+8$	$(^+5, ^+8)$

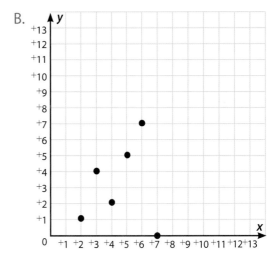

T R Y   I T

Linear Relationships (B)

More Straight Lines

Worked Examples

You can write ordered pairs (x, y) from an input-output table. Then you can graph the ordered pairs on a coordinate plane and see that they lie on a straight line.

PROBLEM Use the input and output values on the table to write ordered pairs in the third column. Then plot the points on the coordinate grid.

Rule: Subtract 5 or $y = x - 5$		
Input x	Output y	(Input, Output) (x, y)
+5	0	?
+6	+1	?
+7	+2	?
+8	+3	?
+9	+4	?
+10	+5	?
+11	+6	?
+12	+7	?
+13	+8	?

Plot the points on the coordinate grid.

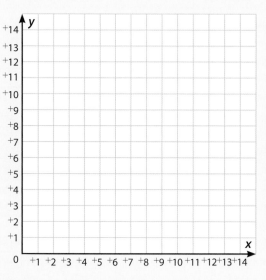

LEARN

1 To write the ordered pairs in the third column of the table, follow these steps:
- Write the value of the *x*-coordinate given in the Input column on the same row.
- Follow the *x*-coordinate with a comma, and skip a space.
- Write the value of the *y*-coordinate from the Output column on the same row.
- Enclose the coordinates with parentheses.

2 To plot the points on the coordinate grid, follow these steps:
- To plot point (⁺5, 0), start at the origin and move right 5 units on the *x*-axis, in a positive direction. From that point, move 0 units on the *y*-axis, not moving up or down. Now draw a point.
- To plot point (⁺6, ⁺1), start at the origin and move right 6 units on the *x*-axis, in a positive direction. From that point, move up 1 unit in a positive direction, parallel to the *y*-axis. Now draw a point.
- Continue until all points have been plotted.

ANSWER

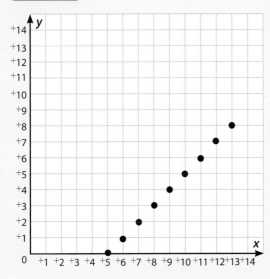

Rule: Subtract 5 or $y = x - 5$		
Input *x*	Output *y*	(Input, Output) (*x*, *y*)
⁺5	0	(⁺5, ⁺0)
⁺6	⁺1	(⁺6, ⁺1)
⁺7	⁺2	(⁺7, ⁺2)
⁺8	⁺3	(⁺8, ⁺3)
⁺9	⁺4	(⁺9, ⁺4)
⁺10	⁺5	(⁺10, ⁺5)
⁺11	⁺6	(⁺11, ⁺6)
⁺12	⁺7	(⁺12, ⁺7)
⁺13	⁺8	(⁺13, ⁺8)

L E A R N

Write the ordered pairs (x, y) to complete the table. Then plot the points on the coordinate grid.

1.

Rule: Add 3 or $y = x + 3$		
Input x	Output y	(Input, Output) (x, y)
0	+3	?
+1	+4	?
+2	+5	?
+3	+6	?
+4	+7	?
+5	+8	?
+6	+9	?
+7	+10	?
+8	+11	?

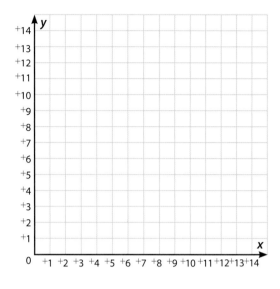

2.

Rule: Subtract 4 or $y = x - 4$		
Input x	Output y	(Input, Output) (x, y)
+14	+10	?
+13	+9	?
+12	+8	?
+11	+7	?
+10	+6	?
+9	+5	?
+8	+4	?
+7	+3	?

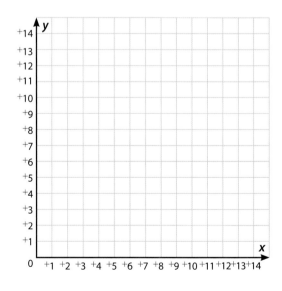

Read the problem and complete the table. (Use the input values and apply the rule given in the table to write the output values in the second column and the ordered pairs in the third column.) Then plot the points on the coordinate grid.

3. Serena attended camp. The number of new friends she made each day was 2 more than the number of days she was there. So on Day 4, Serena made 4 + 2, or 6, new friends. Help Serena complete the table and plot the ordered pairs of (day, new friends) on the coordinate grid.

Rule: Add 2 or $y = x + 2$		
Input x	Output y	(Input, Output) (x, y)
+4	?	?
+5	?	?
+6	?	?
+7	?	?
+8	?	?
+9	?	?
+10	?	?
+11	?	?

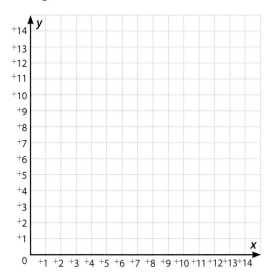

Linear Relationships (B)

Check the Coordinates

Read the problem and follow the directions.

1. Write the ordered pairs to complete the table.

$y = x - 10$		
Input x	Output y	(Input, Output) (x, y)
$^+20$	$^+10$	?
$^+19$	$^+9$	?
$^+18$	$^+8$	?
$^+17$	$^+7$	?
$^+16$	$^+6$	?
$^+15$	$^+5$	?
$^+14$	$^+4$	?

Choose the answer.

2. Joyce plotted 3 points from the equation $y = 3 \times x$ on this coordinate grid. She drew a straight line through the points. Which ordered pair would also be on this line?

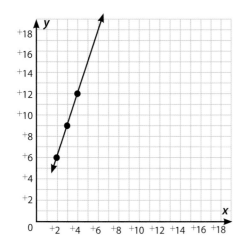

A. $(0, {}^+18)$ B. $(^+6, {}^+18)$ C. $(^+9, {}^+18)$ D. $(^+6, {}^+6)$

TRY IT

3. Identify the graph that matches the equation in the table.

y = x − 7		
Input **x**	**Output** **y**	**(Input, Output)** **(x, y)**
⁺12	⁺5	?
⁺11	⁺4	?
⁺10	⁺3	?
⁺9	⁺2	?
⁺8	⁺1	?
⁺7	0	?

A.
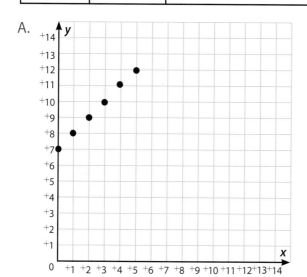

B.
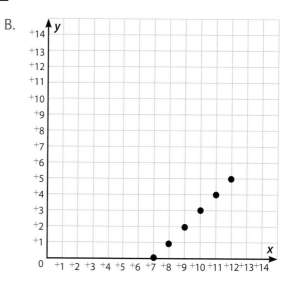

T R Y I T

4. Which correctly graphs $y = x - 8$?

A.

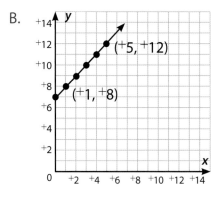

(+12, +5)

(+8, +1)

B.

(+5, +12)

(+1, +8)

C.

(+12, +4)

(+9, +1)

5. Which correctly graphs $y = x - 9$?

A.

(+14, +6)

(+10, +2)

B.

(+14, +5)

(+10, +1)

C.

(+5, +14)

(+1, +10)

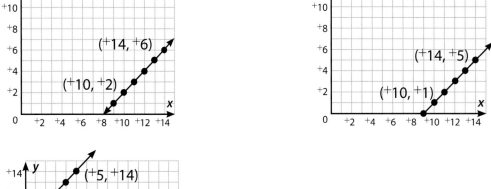

TRY IT

6. Parker plotted 3 points from the equation $y = x + 3$ on this coordinate grid. He drew a straight line through the points. Which ordered pair would also be on this line?

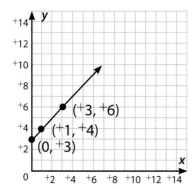

A. $(^+1, ^+3)$

B. $(^+3, ^+3)$

C. $(^+9, ^+3)$

D. $(^+6, ^+9)$

7. Jen plotted 3 points from the equation $y = 3 \times x + 1$ on this coordinate grid. She drew a straight line through the points. Which ordered pair would also be on this line?

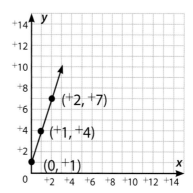

A. $(^+3, ^+10)$

B. $(^+3, ^+3)$

C. $(^+4, ^+7)$

D. $(^+5, ^+11)$

T R Y   I T

Perimeters of Polygons

Measure Perimeter

You can use a ruler to find the perimeter of a polygon. First you measure each side of the outside border of the figure. Be sure to measure with the unit mentioned in the problem, centimeter or inch. Then you find the sum of the lengths of the sides and include the unit in your answer.

PROBLEM Use a dual-scale ruler to find the perimeter of this figure in centimeters.

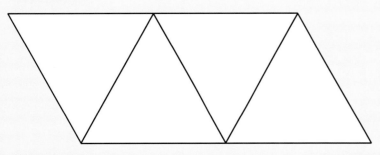

SOLUTION

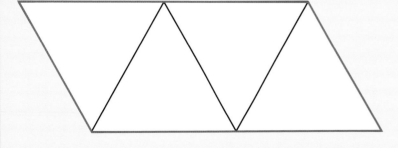

L E A R N

1. Use the metric edge of a dual-scale ruler.

2. Measure each side of the outside border of the figure. Record each measure.
   - upper side, 8 cm
   - right side, 4 cm
   - lower side, 8 cm
   - left side, 4 cm

3. Find the sum of the lengths of the sides.

ANSWER The perimeter of the figure is 24 cm.

Use a dual-scale ruler to solve.

1. What is the perimeter of this figure in centimeters?

2. What is the perimeter of this figure in inches?

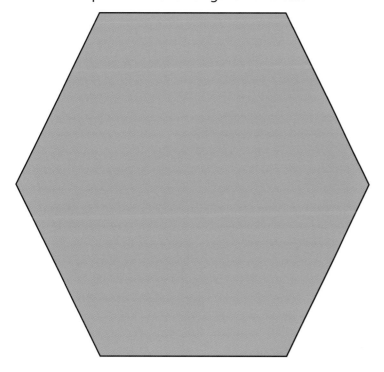

L E A R N

3. What is the perimeter of this figure in centimeters?

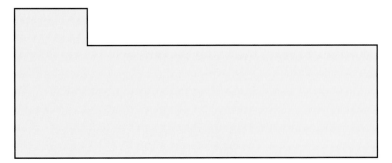

4. What is the perimeter of this figure in inches?

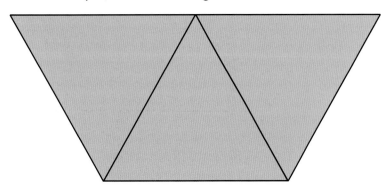

5. What is the perimeter of the shaded part of this figure in centimeters?

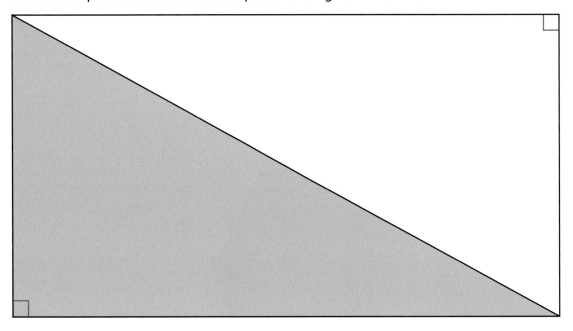

Perimeters of Polygons

Perimeter Practice

Use a ruler to find the perimeter of the figure in centimeters.

1.

2.

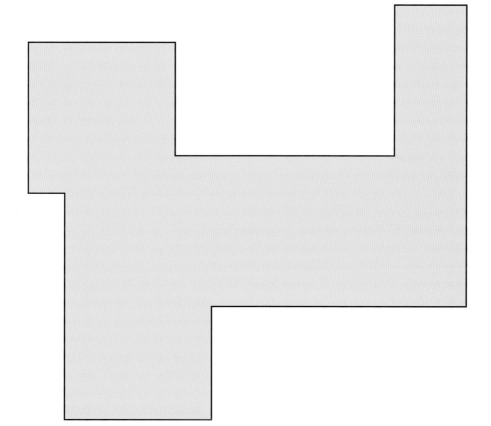

TRY IT

Use a ruler to find the perimeter of the figure in inches.

3.

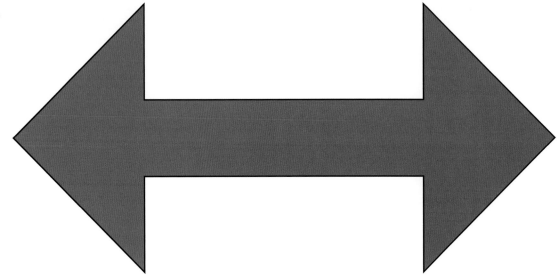

Solve.

4. The rectangle and the hexagon have the same perimeter.
   What are the lengths of the sides of the rectangle that are unmarked?

7 yd

7 yd

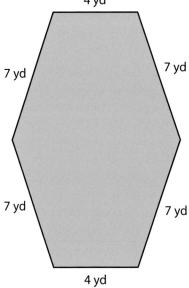

4 yd

7 yd   7 yd

7 yd   7 yd

4 yd

5. What is the perimeter of this parallelogram?

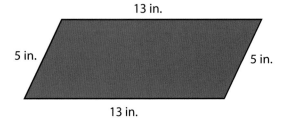

13 in.

5 in.   5 in.

13 in.

TRY IT

Choose the answer.

6. The length of one side of the square is equal to the length of 6 arrows. If each arrow represents 1 unit, what is the perimeter of the square?

   A. 6 units
   B. 18 units
   C. 24 units
   D. 36 units

7. What is the perimeter of the shaded rectangle on this grid?

   A. 13 units
   B. 14 units
   C. 26 units
   D. 28 units

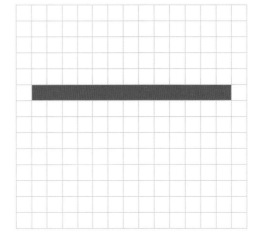

8. What is the perimeter of this polygon?

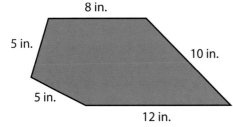

   A. 30 in.
   B. 32 in.
   C. 35 in.
   D. 40 in.

9. What is the perimeter of the polygon if each side is 6 cm?

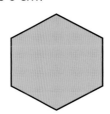

   A. 1 cm
   B. 12 cm
   C. 30 cm
   D. 36 cm

10. The base of Jill's house is in the shape of a regular octagon. Each side of the octagon measures 25 feet. Find the perimeter of the base of Jill's house.

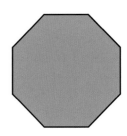

   A. 100 ft
   B. 150 ft
   C. 200 ft
   D. 250 ft

11. Which triangle has the same perimeter as the green triangle?

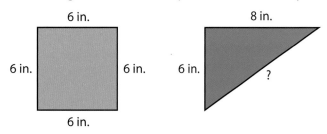

A. 3 3 3

B. 3 3 2

C. 5 4 2

D. 3 2 2

12. The triangle has the same perimeter as the square.

6 in.

6 in.   6 in.

6 in.

8 in.

6 in.   ?

What is the length of the unknown side of the triangle?

A. 6 in.   B. 10 in.   C. 14 in.   D. 24 in.

13. All angles shown on the figure are right angles.

What is the perimeter of the figure?

A. 16 ft

B. 18 ft

C. 20 ft

D. 22 ft

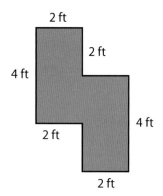

2 ft

2 ft

4 ft

2 ft

4 ft

2 ft

14. Michele is looking for a rug with a perimeter of 24 feet.

Which rectangular rug has a perimeter of 24 feet?

A.

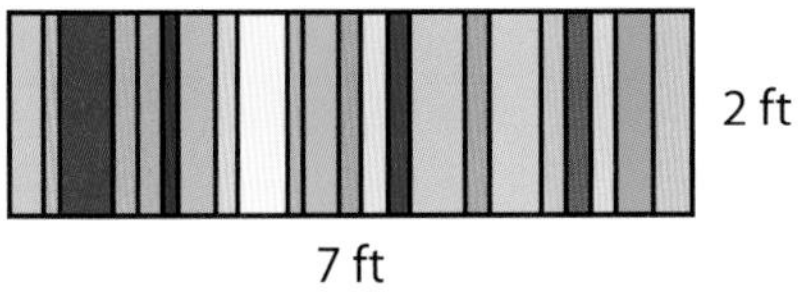

7 ft

2 ft

B.

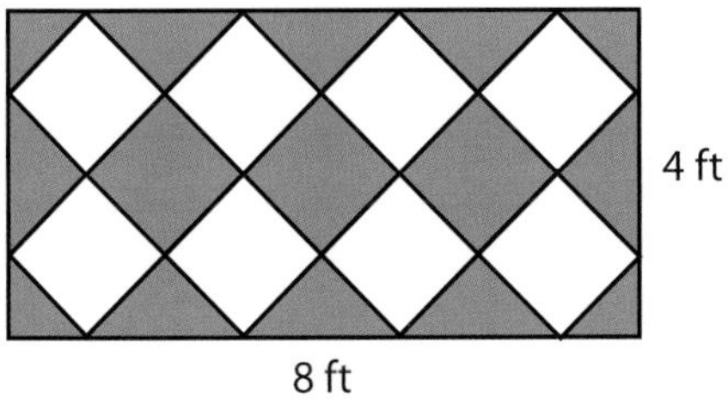

8 ft

4 ft

C.

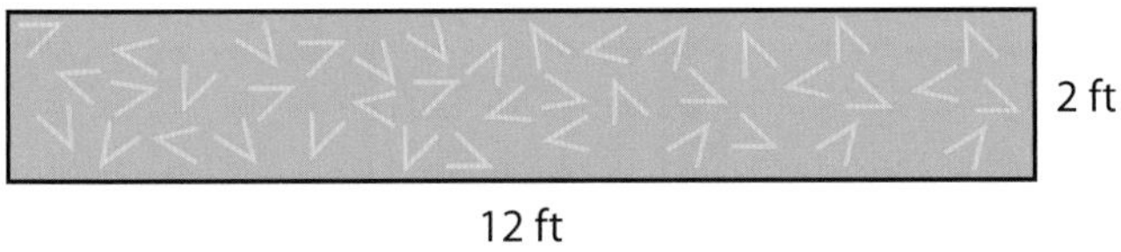

12 ft

2 ft

D.

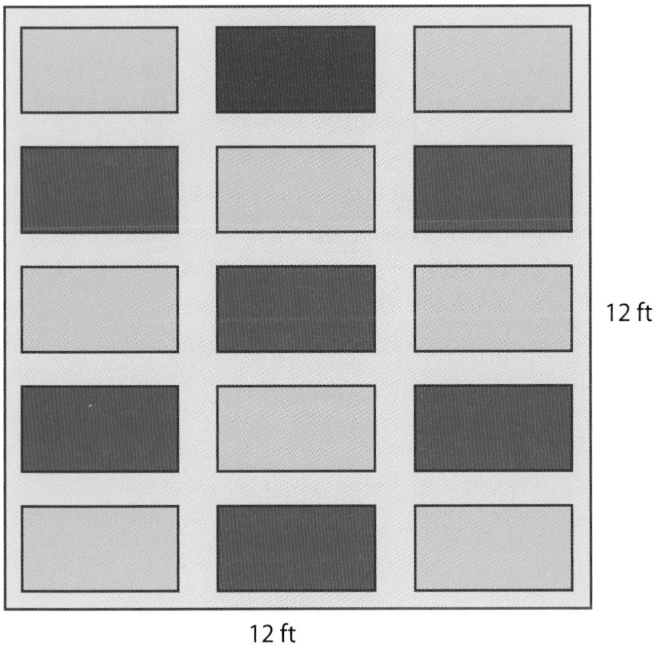

12 ft

12 ft

T R Y   I T

Formulas for Perimeter (A)

Find the Perimeters

Solve.

1. What is the perimeter of this rectangle?

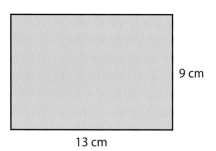

9 cm

13 cm

2. What is the perimeter of this rectangle?

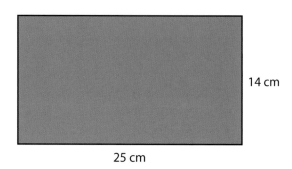

14 cm

25 cm

3. What is the perimeter of this square?

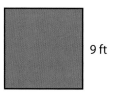

9 ft

4. What is the perimeter of this square?

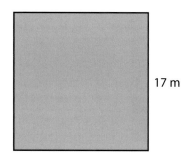

17 m

5. Chuck wants to put a fence around his square garden. One side of his garden measures 3 meters. How much fence will Chuck need?

Find the perimeter. Use a formula, or equation, if you wish.
Note: Diagrams are not drawn to scale.

6.

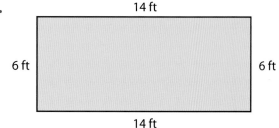

14 ft

6 ft   6 ft

14 ft

7.

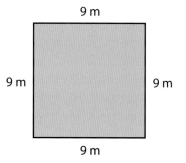

9 m

9 m   9 m

9 m

TRY IT

8.

35 cm
6 cm | | 6 cm
35 cm

9.

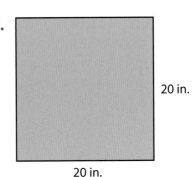

20 in.

20 in.

Choose the answer.

10. Jordan needs to find the perimeter of a large rectangular table represented by the sketch. Which statement describes how she could correctly calculate the perimeter?

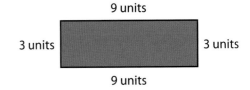

9 units
3 units | | 3 units
9 units

   A. Add $9 + 3$.

   B. Multiply 9×3.

   C. Add $9 + 9 + 3 + 3$.

   D. Multiply $9 \times 9 \times 3 \times 3$.

11. Mrs. Vasquez needs to determine the perimeter of the rectangular window shown so she can buy wood trim to go around it.

   Which equation could Mrs. Vasquez use to determine the perimeter of the window?

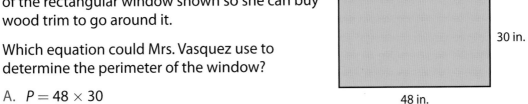

30 in.

48 in.

   A. $P = 48 \times 30$

   B. $P = 48 + 30$

   C. $P = 48 + 30 + 48$

   D. $P = 48 + 48 + 30 + 30$

12. What is the perimeter of the rectangle?

   A. 11 ft

   B. 20 ft

   C. 22 ft

   D. 28 ft

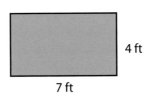

4 ft

7 ft

T R Y I T

13. Aldo folded a paper in half, then he cut out a rectangle along the fold. What is the perimeter of the cut rectangle when it is unfolded?

A. 5 in.

B. 7 in.

C. 10 in.

D. 14 in.

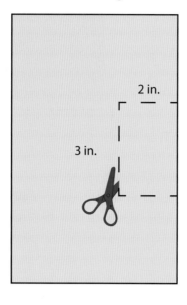

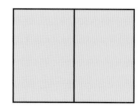

14. Mrs. Anderson wants to install a fence around her square yard. One side of the yard measures 36 feet. How much feet of fencing does she need?

A. 72 ft

B. 144 ft

C. 288 ft

D. 1,296 ft

Read the problem and follow the directions.

15. Maria used this formula to find the perimeter of a rectangular game board:

$(2 \times 5) + (2 \times 8) = 26$; Perimeter is 26 inches.

Sketch and label Maria's game board. Then write another equation that you can use to find the perimeter of the game board.

TRY IT

Formulas for Perimeter (B)

Apply Perimeter Formulas

Worked Examples

You can use formulas to find the perimeter of geometric shapes. First you draw and label a diagram. Then you write a formula and replace the variables with the dimensions from the diagram. Next you compute the perimeter.

PROBLEM What is the perimeter of a rectangular picture frame with these dimensions?

9 in.

12 in.

SOLUTION 1

Add the lengths of the sides to find the perimeter of a rectangle.

$P = l + l + w + w$
$P = 12 + 12 + 9 + 9$
$P = 42$

ANSWER The perimeter of the picture frame is 42 inches.

SOLUTION 2

Add (2 × length) + (2 × width) to find the perimeter of a rectangle.

$P = (2 \times l) + (2 \times w)$
$P = (2 \times 12) + (2 \times 9)$
$P = 24 + 18$
$P = 42$

ANSWER The perimeter of the picture frame is 42 inches.

Complete the equation to find the perimeter of the figure.

1.

8.5 ft

5.5 ft

$P = l + w + l + w$
$P = \underline{\ ?\ } + 5.5 + 8.5 + \underline{\ ?\ }$
$P = \underline{\ ?\ }$

The perimeter is _?_ feet.

L E A R N

Write a perimeter formula for the figure. Replace the variables in your formula with the corresponding given measures. Then find the perimeter.

2. The rectangle below has a width of 5 centimeters and a length of 22 centimeters.

3.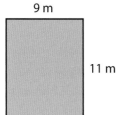
    9 m
    11 m

4.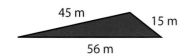
    45 m
    15 m
    56 m

5.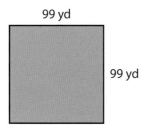
    99 yd
    99 yd

Solve.

6. Trudy sewed together two quilt squares like the ones shown. She then put fringe around the outside of the new rectangular piece of material. How many inches of fringe did Trudy use?

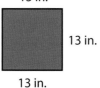
13 in.
13 in.   13 in.
13 in.

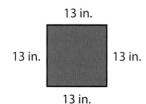
13 in.
13 in.   13 in.
13 in.

7. Stephen folds a piece of cardboard and then cuts out a triangle as shown. What is the perimeter of the triangular piece of cardboard?

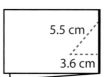
5.5 cm
3.6 cm

You can use formulas to find the perimeter of geometric shapes. First you draw and label a diagram. Then you write a formula and replace the variables with the dimensions from the diagram. Next you compute the perimeter.

PROBLEM Karl wants to put a fence around a rectangular garden that is 6 feet by 9 feet. How long should the fence be?

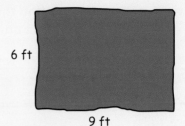

6 ft

9 ft

SOLUTION 1

1. Draw and label a diagram.

2. Use the perimeter formula
   $P = (2 \times l) + (2 \times w)$.

   $P = (2 \times l) + (2 \times w)$
   $P = (2 \times 9) + (2 \times 6)$
   $P = 18 + 12$
   $P = 30$

ANSWER The perimeter is 30 ft, so the fence will be 30 ft long.

SOLUTION 2

1. Draw and label a diagram.

2. Use the perimeter formula
   $P = 2 \times (l + w)$.

   $P = 2 \times (l + w)$
   $P = 2 \times (9 + 6)$
   $P = 2 \times 15$
   $P = 30$

ANSWER The perimeter is 30 ft, so the fence will be 30 ft long.

Complete the equation to solve.

8. A swimming pool is a rectangle 100 feet long and 45 feet wide. What is the perimeter of the pool?

   $P = (2 \times l) + (2 \times w)$
   $P = (2 \times \underline{?}) + (2 \times \underline{?})$
   $P = \underline{?} + \underline{?}$
   $P = \underline{?}$

   The perimeter of the pool is $\underline{?}$ ft.

Use a formula or equation to solve. Show your work.

9. A park is shaped like a square with sides that are 5.3 kilometers long. What is the length of a bike path that goes around the outside border of the park?

10. Jessica's bedroom is 4.6 meters long and 3 meters wide. She puts a wallpaper border around the perimeter of the room near the ceiling. How long is the wallpaper border?

L E A R N

Formulas for Perimeter (B)

Solve with Perimeter Formulas

 Use a formula, or equation, to find the perimeter. Show your work.
Write the answer with the correct unit.

1.

12.25 m

1.5 m

2. Charlie builds a sandbox for his grandson. It is a square with sides
5 feet long. What is the perimeter of the sandbox?

Read the problem and follow the directions.

3. Mr. Tunison is building a house. Part of the floor plan for the house is
shown. Mr. Tunison is going to put carpet tape under the carpet
around the sides of Room A and under the carpet around the hallway.
How many feet of carpet tape does Mr. Tunison need? Show how to use
formulas to find the answer.

16 ft   15 ft

Room A   15 ft

17 ft

Hallway   5 ft

TRY IT

4. Find the missing measurements. Then find the perimeter.
Explain how you got your answer.

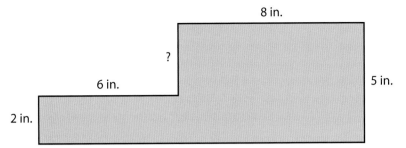

8 in.

?

6 in.

5 in.

2 in.

Choose the answer.

5. Mrs. Collins has two connected rectangular pens for her farm animals. The pens are shown below. She wants to surround the pair of pens with new fence, but she does not want to put a new fence between the pens.

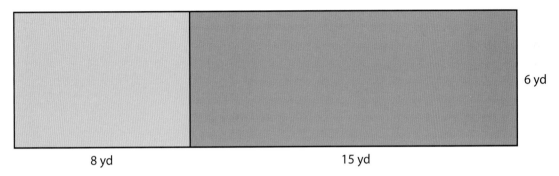

6 yd

8 yd

15 yd

What should Mrs. Collins do to find the total length of fencing needed to surround the pair of pens?

A. Add all the numbers shown in the drawing.

B. Find the perimeter of the smaller pen, and then add 21.

C. Add the perimeters of the pens, and then subtract 6.

D. Add the numbers shown in the drawing, and then multiply by 2.

6. What is the perimeter of the swimming pool?

A. 50 ft

B. 100 ft

C. 200 ft

D. 600 ft

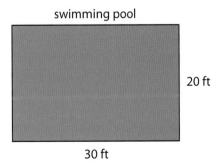

swimming pool

20 ft

30 ft

TRY IT

7. Ron installed wallpaper border around the top of his bedroom. If the rectangular bedroom measures 12 feet by 14 feet, how many feet of border did he use?

   A. 26 ft   B. 48 ft   C. 52 ft   D. 56 ft

8. Tirey has a pool that measures 48 meters long and 15 meters wide. What is the perimeter of the pool?

   A. 63 m

   B. 96 m

   C. 116 m

   D. 126 m

9. Damon built a dog house. The base was a perfect square that was 6 feet long on each side. What was the perimeter of the dog house?

   A. 12 ft

   B. 18 ft

   C. 24 ft

   D. 36 ft

10. Manuella compared the perimeter of the figures below.

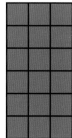

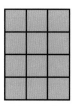

Figure B

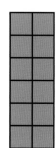

Figure A   Figure C

Which sentence is true?

   A. The perimeter of Figure B is less than the perimeter of Figure A.

   B. The perimeter of Figure C is greater than the perimeter of Figure A.

   C. The perimeter of Figure A is less than the perimeter of Figure C.

   D. The perimeter of Figure A is equal to the perimeter of Figure C.

11. Which equation would **not** correctly calculate the perimeter of this rectangle?

5 cm

7 cm

   A. $P = 2 \times 5 + 7$

   B. $P = 7 + 5 + 7 + 5$

   C. $P = 2 \times (7 + 5)$

   D. $P = 2 \times 7 + 2 \times 5$

12. Which **two** equations could be used to calculate the perimeter of this square?

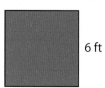

6 ft

   A. $P = 6 \times 6$

   B. $P = 6 + 6$

   C. $P = 6 \times 4$

   D. $P = 6 + 6 + 6 + 6$

TRY IT

13. Terrence compared the perimeters of the shaded figures below.

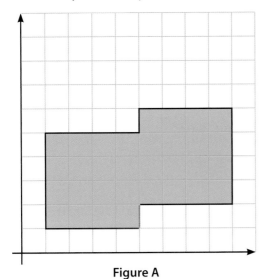

Figure A

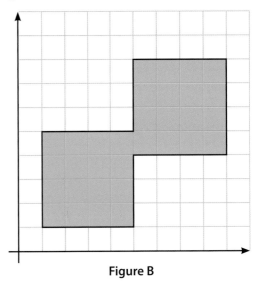

Figure B

Which sentence is true?

A. The perimeter of Figure A is greater than the perimeter of Figure B.

B. The perimeter of Figure A is less than the perimeter of Figure B.

14. Which statement about these rectangles is true?

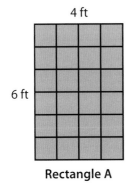

Rectangle A

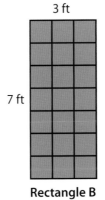

Rectangle B

A. The perimeter of Rectangle A is greater than the perimeter of Rectangle B.

B. The perimeter of Rectangle A is the same as the perimeter of Rectangle B.

C. The area of Rectangle A is the same as the area of Rectangle B.

D. The area of Rectangle B is greater than the area of Rectangle A.

TRY IT

Formulas for Area (A)

Solve with Area Formulas

Use a formula, or equation, to find the area. Show your work.

1.

16 m

5 m   5 m

16 m

2.

25 cm

25 cm

3. Find the area of a rectangle that is 21 yards long by 9 yards wide.

Solve.

4. Briana helps her mother make a quilt. The quilt is 6 feet wide and 12 feet long. What is the area of the quilt?

5. Use formulas to find the area of the compound figure. Show your work. Explain how you found your answer.

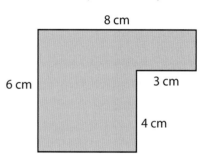

8 cm

6 cm   3 cm

4 cm

6. What is the area of this rectangle?

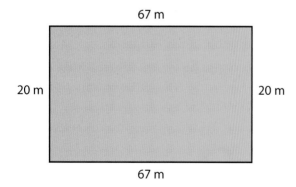

67 m

20 m   20 m

67 m

TRY IT

Choose the answer.

7. Shawn drew a diagram showing the dimensions of his closet and Emma's closet.

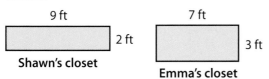

Shawn's closet

Emma's closet

Which statement about the closets is true?

A. Emma's closet has a greater perimeter and area.

B. Shawn's closet has a greater perimeter and area.

C. Emma's closet has a greater area but a smaller perimeter.

D. Shawn's closet has a greater area but a smaller perimeter.

8. Jennifer measured a rectangular garden in her backyard. The plot is shown.

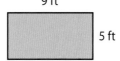

Which sentence gives the correct area and perimeter of Jennifer's garden?

A. The area is 14 ft² and the perimeter is 28 ft.

B. The area is 28 ft² and the perimeter is 45 ft.

C. The area is 45 ft² and the perimeter is 14 ft.

D. The area is 45 ft² and the perimeter is 28 ft.

9. Justice measured his rectangular vegetable garden.

3 m

5 m

Which statement is true about the area and perimeter of Justice's garden?

A. The perimeter is 8 m and the area is 15 m².

B. The perimeter is 16 m and the area is 15 m².

C. The perimeter is 15 m and the area is 16 m².

D. The perimeter is 16 m and the area is 8 m².

10. On the grid, the shaded squares represent Nancy's closet floor.

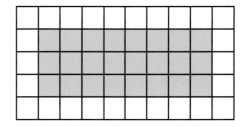

Nancy says the perimeter of the closet floor is 22 units and the area is 24 square units. Which sentence best explains if she is correct, and why or why not?

A. Yes, she is correct because the area of a floor is always greater than its perimeter.

B. Yes, she is correct because 24 is the number of squares needed to cover the surface, and 22 is the sum of all the sides.

C. No, she is incorrect because 22 is the number of squares needed to cover the surface, and 24 is the sum of all the sides.

D. No, she is incorrect because the perimeter of a floor is always greater than its area.

T R Y   I T

11. Which rectangle has an area smaller than the one shown here?

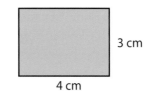

3 cm

4 cm

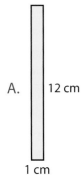

A. 12 cm

1 cm

B. 4 cm

4 cm

C. 5 cm

3 cm

D. 2 cm

5 cm

12. The dimensions of a rectangular tablecloth are shown below.

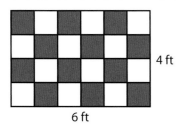

4 ft

6 ft

Which computation could be used to determine the area of the tablecloth?

A. Multiply 6 by 4.

B. Add 6 and 4.

C. Multiply 6 by 4, and then multiply by 2.

D. Add 6 and 4, and then multiply by 2.

13. Yolanda wants to water the grass in her rectangular backyard. Below is a diagram of the backyard.

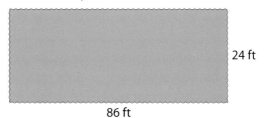

24 ft

86 ft

What is the area of Yolanda's backyard?

A. 220 ft²

B. 516 ft²

C. 1,884 ft²

D. 2,064 ft²

14. What is the area of the figure below?

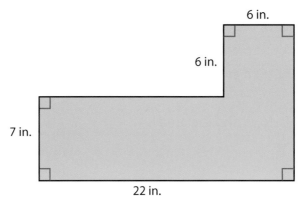

6 in.

6 in.

7 in.

22 in.

A. 252 in²   B. 190 in²   C. 174 in²   D. 154 in²

TRY IT

Formulas for Area (B)

Area of Complex Figures

Worked Examples

You can use area formulas to find the area of a complex figure. First you divide the figure into smaller rectangles or squares. Then you use formulas to find the area of the smaller figures. Next you find the sum of the areas.

PROBLEM Madeline wants to paste a flat piece of plastic to the front of the project display board shown. All angles are right angles. How many square inches of plastic does Madeline need?

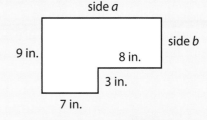

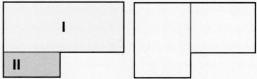

SOLUTION

1 Divide the figure into smaller rectangles or squares. Two ways to divide the figure are shown shown here. This solution is for the shaded figure on the left.

2 Use the given dimensions to find the dimensions that are not given.

3 Find the area of each rectangle.

Rectangle I	Rectangle II
$A = l \times w$	$A = l \times w$
$A = 15$ in. $\times$ 6 in.	$A = 7$ in. $\times$ 3 in.
$A = 90$ in^2	$A = 21$ in^2

4 Add the areas of the two rectangles to find the total area.
90 in^2 $+ 21$ in^2 $= 111$ in^2

side _a_
- The 7 in. side and the 8 in. side, together, are the same length as side _a_.
- Add $7 + 8 = 15$.
- The length of side _a_ is 15 in.
- Let 15 in. be the length of Rectangle I.

side _b_
- The lengths of side _b_ and the 3 in. side together are the same length as the 9 in. side. So 9 in. minus 3 in. is the length of side _b_.
- Subtract $9 - 3 = 6$.
- The length of side _b_ is 6 in.
- Let 6 in. be the width of Rectangle I.

ANSWER Madeline needs 111 in^2 of plastic to cover the front of the project display board.

L E A R N

Find the area. Show your work.

1.

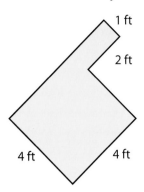

1 ft
2 ft
4 ft   4 ft

Rectangle	Square
$A = ? \times ?$	$A = ? \times ?$
$A = ? \times ?$	$A = ? \times ?$
$A = ?$	$A = ?$

Total area $= ?$ ft² $+ ?$ ft² $= ?$ ft²

2. The pyramid El Castillo stands in the Yucatan peninsula of Mexico. It has a square base with four staircases that jut out, one on each side. Joe drew an outline of a complex figure like the El Castillo pyramid. The dimensions are approximate. Use Joe's diagram to find the approximate total area that the base of the pyramid covers.

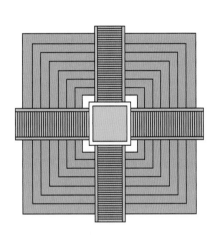

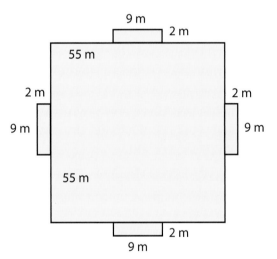

9 m
2 m
55 m
2 m   2 m
9 m   9 m
55 m
2 m
9 m

Square	Rectangle
$A = ? \times ?$	$A = ? \times ?$
$A = ?$	$A = ?$

The total area $= ?$ m² $+ (4 \times ?$ m²$)$

$\qquad\qquad = ?$ m² $+ ?$ m²

$\qquad\qquad = ?$ m²

Formulas for Area (B)

Interpret and Use Formulas

Find the perimeter and area of the figure. Explain how you found your answer.

1.

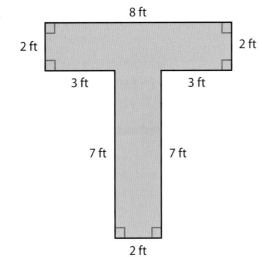

2.

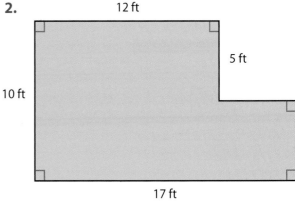

Use Problems 1 and 2 to solve.

3. Which has the greater area?

4. Which has the lesser perimeter?

Solve. Explain how you found your answer.

5. The plastic flag on the mailbox at Janine's house is shown. Find the area of the entire figure.

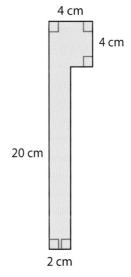

Solve.

6. What is the area of a rectangular field which is 25 meters long and 15 meters wide?

7. What is the area of a square if one side is 14 centimeters long?

293

TRY IT

Choose the answer.

8. A rectangle is 32 meters long and 4 meters wide. Which equation represents the area (A) of the rectangle?

A. $A = 32 \times 4$

B. $32 = (4 \times A) \times 4$

C. $32 = A \times 4$

D. $A = (2 \times 4) + (2 \times 32)$

9. Which rectangle has an area greater than the one shown?

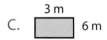
2 m | 15 m

A.
7 m / 4 m

B.
13 m / 3 m

C.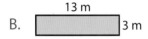
3 m / 6 m

D.
16 m / 1 m

10. Which figure has an area greater than the one shown?

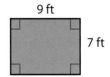
9 ft / 7 ft

A.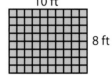
10 ft / 8 ft

B.
8 ft / 6 ft

C.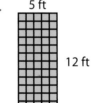
5 ft / 12 ft

D.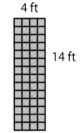
4 ft / 14 ft

11. What is the area of the figure?

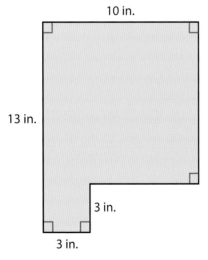
10 in. / 13 in. / 3 in. / 3 in.

A. 109 in²

B. 100 in²

C. 90 in²

D. 46 in²

12. What is the area of the figure?

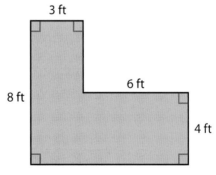
3 ft / 8 ft / 6 ft / 4 ft

A. 60 ft²

B. 50 ft²

C. 48 ft²

D. 24 ft²

TRY IT

13. What is the area of the figure?

4 cm

4 cm

5 cm

16 cm

A. 80 cm²   B. 84 cm²

C. 88 cm²   D. 96 cm²

14. What is the area of the figure?

6 m

5 m

2 m

9 m

A. 36 m²

B. 30 m²

C. 12 m²

D. 9 m²

15. Mr. McBean is fencing a rectangular pasture for his horses. What is the area of the pasture that will be used for Mr. McBean's horses?

45 ft

25 ft

25 ft

45 ft

A. 140 ft²   B. 140 yd²

C. 1,125 ft²   D. 1,125 yd²

T R Y I T

Compare Area and Perimeter
Same Perimeter, Different Areas

You can use 1-inch square tiles to build rectangles or squares with the same perimeter but different areas. You can also use 1-inch grid paper to draw rectangles or squares with the same perimeter but different areas. Then you can enter your data in a table to compare the areas of these shapes.

PROBLEM Build or draw rectangles or squares that each has a perimeter of 14 inches. Use the table to help you write the dimensions of each shape. Then write the area of each shape.

Same Perimeter, Different Areas				
Name of shape	Length (l)	Width (w)	Area (A)	Perimeter (P)
Shape 1	$l = ?$ in.	$w = ?$ in.	$A = ?$ in^2	$P = 14$ in.
Shape 2	$l = ?$ in.	$w = ?$ in.	$A = ?$ in^2	$P = 14$ in.
Shape 3	$l = ?$ in.	$w = ?$ in.	$A = ?$ in^2	$P = 14$ in.

SOLUTION

1 Use the guess-and-test method of problem solving. Estimate how many tiles it will take to build a rectangle or square that has a perimeter of 14 inches. Count out the tiles and build a rectangle or square. You can also draw a rectangle or square on grid paper.

2 Starting at one corner of your shape, count the 1-inch lengths that form a border completely around the shape, or the perimeter of the shape.

3 If the perimeter of your shape is less than 14 inches, add 1 or more tiles. If the perimeter of your shape is greater than 14 inches, take away 1 or more tiles. Continue this process until you build a rectangle or square with a perimeter of 14 inches.

4 Record the dimensions of your first shape.

5 Count the 1-inch square tiles that make up the shape, or the area of the shape. You may also use the formula $A = l \times w$ or the formula $A = s \times s$. Record the area of the shape.

6 Continue to build rectangles that each have a 14-inch perimeter. The dimensions must be different for each shape.

LEARN

7 Record the dimensions and areas of each new shape, but do not record a shape twice. For example, a 5-inch by 2-inch rectangle should not also be recorded as a 2-inch by 5-inch rectangle.

ANSWER

Same Perimeter, Different Areas				
Name of shape	Length (*l*)	Width (*w*)	Area (*A*)	Perimeter (*P*)
Shape 1	*l* = 6 in.	*w* = 1 in.	*A* = 6 in²	*P* = 14 in.
Shape 2	*l* = 5 in.	*w* = 2 in.	*A* = 10 in²	*P* = 14 in.
Shape 3	*l* = 4 in.	*w* = 3 in.	*A* = 12 in²	*P* = 14 in.

Use 1-inch square tiles or 1-inch grid paper to solve the problem.

1. Build or draw rectangles or squares that each have a perimeter of 16 inches. Use the table to record the dimensions of each shape. Then record the area of each shape.

Same Perimeter, Different Areas				
Name of shape	Length (*l*)	Width (*w*)	Area (*A*)	Perimeter (*P*)
Shape 1	*l* = ? in.	*w* = ? in.	*A* = ? in²	*P* = 16 in.
Shape 2	*l* = ? in.	*w* = ? in.	*A* = ? in²	*P* = 16 in.
Shape 3	*l* = ? in.	*w* = ? in.	*A* = ? in²	*P* = 16 in.
Shape 4	*s* = ? in.	*s* = ? in.	*A* = ? in²	*P* = 16 in.

2. Build or draw rectangles or squares that each have a perimeter of 8 inches. Use the table to record the dimensions of each shape. Then record the area of each shape.

Same Perimeter, Different Areas				
Name of shape	Length (*l*)	Width (*w*)	Area (*A*)	Perimeter (*P*)
Shape 1	*l* = ? in.	*w* = ? in.	*A* = ? in²	*P* = 8 in.
Shape 2	*s* = ? in.	*s* = ? in.	*A* = ? in²	*P* = 8 in.

L E A R N

Use this table to answer Problems 3 and 4.

Rectangles: Same Perimeter, Different Areas			
Name of shape	Length (l)	Width (w)	Perimeter (P)
Shape 1	9 in.	1 in.	20 in.
Shape 2	8 in.	2 in.	20 in.
Shape 3	7 in.	3 in.	20 in.
Shape 4	6 in.	4 in.	20 in.
Shape 5	5 in.	5 in.	20 in.

3. Which shape has an area of 24 square inches? Use an area formula to explain your answer.

4. The table shows the dimensions of four rectangles and one square that each have a perimeter of 20 inches. Could you use 1-inch square tiles to build a square with a perimeter of 18 inches? Explain your answer.

Solve.

5. A 3-centimeter by 8-centimeter mailing label has a perimeter of 22 centimeters and an area of 24 square centimeters. What are the dimensions of another label that has the same perimeter but a different area?

6. Mr. Liska decides to buy one of the banners listed below. Each has a perimeter of 18 feet. Which banner should Mr. Liska choose if he wants one with the greatest area? Explain your answer.

Color of banner	Length (l)	Width (w)	Perimeter (P)
Yellow	7 ft	2 ft	18 ft
Purple	5 ft	4 ft	18 ft
Orange	8 ft	1 ft	18 ft
Pink	6 ft	3 ft	18 ft

LEARN

Compare Area and Perimeter

Same Area, Different Perimeters

You can use 1-inch square tiles to build rectangles or squares with the same area but different perimeters. You can also use 1-inch grid paper to draw the rectangles or squares with the same area but different perimeters. Then you can enter your data in a table to compare the perimeters of these shapes.

PROBLEM Build or draw rectangles or squares that each has an area of 16 square inches. Use the table to record the dimensions of each shape. Then record the perimeter of each shape.

Same Area, Different Perimeters				
Name of shape	**Length (l)**	**Width (w)**	**Perimeter (P)**	**Area (A)**
Shape 1	$l = ?$ in.	$w = ?$ in.	$P = ?$ in.	$A = 16$ in^2
Shape 2	$l = ?$ in.	$w = ?$ in.	$P = ?$ in.	$A = 16$ in^2
Shape 3	$s = ?$ in.	$s = ?$ in.	$P = ?$ in.	$A = 16$ in^2

SOLUTION

1 Count out 16 tiles or prepare to draw on grid paper. Build or draw a rectangle that has an area of 16 square inches.

2 Use the table to record the rectangle's dimensions. Then starting at one corner of the rectangle, count the 1-inch lengths that form a border completely around the shape, or the perimeter of the shape. You may also use a perimeter formula, such as $P = 2 \times (l + w)$. Record the perimeter of your rectangle.

3 Build or draw a second rectangle with an area of 16 square inches. Do not record a shape twice. For example, an 8-inch by 2-inch rectangle should not also be recorded as a 2-inch by 8-inch rectangle. Record the dimensions and perimeter of the second rectangle.

4 Now build or draw a square with an area of 16 square inches. Record the dimensions and perimeter of the square.

L E A R N

Same Area, Different Perimeters				
Name of shape	Length (*l*)	Width (*w*)	Perimeter (*P*)	Area (*A*)
Shape 1	16 in.	1 in.	34 in.	$A = 16$ in^2
Shape 2	8 in.	2 in.	20 in.	$A = 16$ in^2
Shape 3	4 in.	4 in.	16 in.	$A = 16$ in^2

Use 1-inch square tiles or 1-inch grid paper to solve Problems 1 and 2.

1. Build or draw rectangles that each have an area of 20 square inches. Use the table to record the dimensions of each shape. Then record the perimeter of each shape.

Same Area, Different Perimeters				
Name of rectangle	Length (*l*)	Width (*w*)	Perimeter (*P*)	Area (*A*)
Rectangle 1	*l* = ? in.	*w* = ? in.	*P* = ? in.	$A = 20$ in^2
Rectangle 2	*l* = ? in.	*w* = ? in.	*P* = ? in.	$A = 20$ in^2
Rectangle 3	*l* = ? in.	*w* = ? in.	*P* = ? in.	$A = 20$ in^2

2. Build or draw a rectangle and a square that each have an area of 25 square inches. Use the table to record the dimensions of each shape. Then record the perimeter of each shape.

Same Area, Different Perimeters				
Name of shape	Length (*l*)	Width (*w*)	Perimeter (*P*)	Area (*A*)
Shape 1	*l* = ? in.	*w* = ? in.	*P* = ? in.	$A = 25$ in^2
Shape 2	*s* = ? in.	*s* = ? in.	*P* = ? in.	$A = 25$ in^2

Use this table to answer Problems 3 and 4.

Rectangles: Same Area, Different Perimeters			
Name of rectangle	Length (*l*)	Width (*w*)	Area (*A*)
Rectangle 1	8 in.	6 in.	48 in²
Rectangle 2	12 in.	4 in.	48 in²
Rectangle 3	24 in.	2 in.	48 in²
Rectangle 4	48 in.	1 in.	48 in²

3. Which rectangle has a perimeter of 52 inches? Use a perimeter formula to explain your answer.

4. Which rectangle has the greatest perimeter? Use a perimeter formula to explain your answer.

Solve.

5. Alexander has a garden that is 5 yards by 6 yards. He wants to make another garden with the same area but different dimensions. Should he make a garden that is 10 yards by 3 yards, or one that is 4 yards by 6 yards?

6. Rosa has two rectangular rugs in her house. The two rugs have the same area but different perimeters. Which of the following rugs could belong to Rosa? Explain your answer.

Name of rug	Length (*l*)	Width (*w*)
Blue rug	5 ft	4 ft
Red rug	9 ft	2 ft
Green rug	8 ft	2 ft
Black rug	6 ft	3 ft

LEARN

Compare Area and Perimeter

Area and Perimeter Problems

Answer the question.

1. Do these shapes have the same area or the same perimeter?

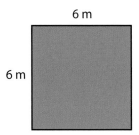
6 m
6 m

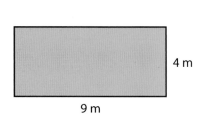
4 m
9 m

2. How are these rectangles alike and different in terms of their perimeters and areas?

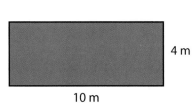
4 m
10 m

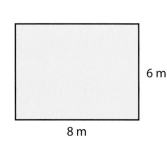
6 m
8 m

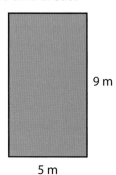
9 m
5 m

Use this rectangle to answer Problems 3 and 4.

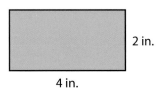
2 in.
4 in.

3. Draw and label a shape that has the same perimeter but a different area.

4. Draw and label a shape that has the same area but a different perimeter.

Choose the answer.

5. Each rectangle and square with the dimensions below has a perimeter of 16 inches. Which rectangle has an area of 12 square inches?

A. 6 in. by 2 in.

B. 5 in. by 3 in.

C. 4 in. by 4 in.

D. 7 in. by 1 in.

TRY IT

6. Which of the following statements is true about these rectangles?

10 ft
3 ft

15 ft
2 ft

A. They have the same area but different perimeters.

B. They have the same perimeter but different areas.

C. They have different areas and perimeters.

D. They have the same areas and perimeters.

7. Which of the following statements is true about these rectangles ?

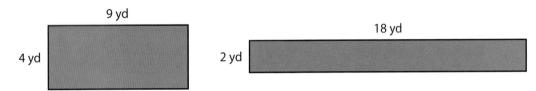

9 yd
4 yd

18 yd
2 yd

A. They have different areas and perimeters.

B. They have the same area but different perimeters.

C. They have the same areas and perimeters.

D. They have the same perimeter but different areas.

8. The listed options give the dimensions of different rectangles with an area of 60 square inches.

Which dimensions will result in the greatest perimeter?

A. 20 in. by 3 in.

B. 10 in. by 6 in.

C. 15 in. by 4 in.

D. 30 in. by 2 in.

9. A rectangle with a length of 7 feet and a width of 4 feet has an area of 28 square feet and a perimeter of 22 feet.

Which **two** rectangles have dimensions that give the same area as this rectangle but different perimeters?

A. 2 ft by 14 ft

B. 28 ft by 1 ft

C. 5 ft by 6 ft

D. 8 ft by 3 ft

10. Each option describes a rectangle with an area of 24 square centimeters.

Which dimensions describe a rectangle with a perimeter of 28 centimeters?

A. 1 cm by 24 cm

B. 2 cm by 12 cm

C. 3 cm by 8 cm

D. 4 cm by 6 cm

TRY IT

11. This square and this rectangle have equal perimeters.

    Based on this information, which statement is true?

    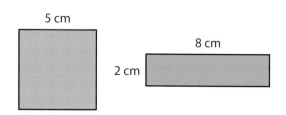
    5 cm
    8 cm
    2 cm

    A. The figures are both squares.

    B. The figures have different areas.

    C. The figures have the same dimensions.

    D. The figures have different angle measures.

12. Which of the following statements is true about these rectangles?

    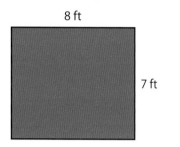
    8 ft
    7 ft

    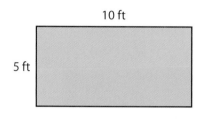
    10 ft
    5 ft

    A. They have different perimeters
       and different areas.

    B. They have different areas but the
       same perimeter.

    C. They have the same perimeter and
       the same area.

    D. They have the same area but
       different perimeters.

13. Each shape has a perimeter of 26 feet. Which shape has the greatest area?

    A.
    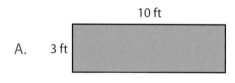
    10 ft
    3 ft

    B.

    7 ft
    6 ft

    C.
    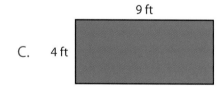
    9 ft
    4 ft

    D.
    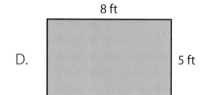
    8 ft
    5 ft

14. This rectangle has a perimeter
    of 40 centimeters and an area
    of 84 square centimeters.

    Which rectangle also has a perimeter of
    40 centimeters but has a different area?

    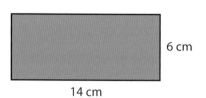
    6 cm
    14 cm

    A. 12 cm by 8 cm   B. 25 cm by 15 cm   C. 10 cm by 4 cm   D. 42 cm by 2 cm

TRY IT